The Colours in me

The Colours in me

WRITING AND POETRY BY ADOPTED CHILDREN AND YOUNG PEOPLE

Edited by Perlita Harris

BAAF
ADOPTION
& FOSTERING

Published by
British Association for Adoption & Fostering
(BAAF)
Saffron House
6–10 Kirby Street
London EC1N 8TS
www.baaf.org.uk

Charity registration 275689 (England & Wales) and SC039337 (Scotland)

British Library Cataloguing in Publication Data
A catalogue record for this book is available from the British Library

ISBN 9781 905664 59 7

Project management by Miranda Davies, BAAF
Illustration on cover by Veronica Whitehead
Designed by Andrew Haig & Associates
Typeset by Fravashi Aga
Printed in Great Britain by Lavenham Press
Trade distribution by Turnaround Publisher Services, Unit 3,
Olympia Trading Estate, Coburg Road, London N22 6TZ

BAAF is the leading UK-wide membership organisation for all those concerned
with adoption, fostering and child care issues.

To Tin Nga
天娜
with my love

and to my parents,
Ann and Jack Harris

Contents

Note about the editor

Perlita Harris is a transracially adopted adult who joined her adoptive family when she was almost five years old. She has reunited with her Papaji and both her paternal and maternal extended families.

Perlita is a registered social worker who specialised in adoption and adoption support prior to undertaking a PhD in Social Work at the University of Warwick. She also holds a BA (Hons), Post Graduate Diploma, MSc, Certificate of Qualification in Social Work (CQSW), Certificate in Systemic Practice and the Advanced Award in Social Work (Research Pathway).

Perlita has written a number of journal articles on service users' views and experiences of adoption support services. Her first book, *In Search of Belonging: Reflections by transracially adopted people*, was published by BAAF in 2006. Perlita is currently a lecturer in social work at Goldsmiths, University of London.

She may be reached at Perlita.Harris2@btinternet.com.

Acknowledgements

The inspiration for this collection originated in the summer 2006 in a conversation with Ann Gillham, adoption social worker (Barnardo's Jigsaw), adoptive mother and friend. We talked about the need for a book for adopted children and young people that could be read either alone or with the help of an adoptive parent.

I would like to extend my warmest thanks and appreciation to all the individual social work practitioners, adoption-related email groups, adoption agencies and adoption support agencies that spread the word about the call for submissions through websites, newsletters, email lists and direct contact with service users and practitioners. There will be many people, groups and agencies whose names are unknown to me: I thank them all. Regretfully, those agencies and groups whose support I know of and who I would like to thank individually are too numerous to name.

A huge thanks goes to the adoptive mothers and fathers for supporting and encouraging their children to participate in this project, for being open to hearing their children's happiness and sorrow, and for not shying away from emotions and questions that writing or drawing may have given rise to. Without their support this collection would not have been possible.

At BAAF I would like to thank Savita de Sousa and Roana Roach; Isabelle Rameau, Editor of *Be My Parent*; Shaila Shah, Director of Publications, for her enthusiasm and support; and Miranda Davies for her thoughtful work as BAAF editor.

I am very thankful to Rhona Cameron for her insightful, pertinent and poignant Foreword.

A very special thank you goes to Veronica Whitehead (age 10) for allowing her picture and its title, *The Colours in Me*, to form the basis of the cover.

Finally, my greatest thanks and deepest appreciation go to all the children and young people who had the courage and strength to write about, speak about or draw their experiences of adoption. You are an amazing group of children and young people and you should be proud of what you have each achieved!

Perlita Harris
November 2008

Foreword

I was adopted a couple of months after my birth in 1965. Although I loved my adoptive parents very much and they loved me, I felt most of my young life crippled by a sense of loss I didn't understand. This feeling of loss, which is so often compounded by guilt and the fear of the betrayal of our adopted parents, made me feel incredibly isolated and detached from the world I occupied. The desperate longing to fit in, yet the overwhelming feeling of detachment, perpetuated an anxiety that I acted out in many forms, which dominated my young life at a time when I should have been relatively carefree.

Now in my early 40s, only through psychoanalysis and sobriety have I come to terms with my feelings of unwantedness. I have learned not to project these uncomfortable feelings onto other people, pushing them away in order to control my losses. Through my healing I have slowly begun to learn about love, how to keep people and how to see things through rather than destroying them mid-term.

The complexity of adoption and the void it leaves us with must be hard for those not adopted to comprehend. The void can stay with us our entire lives, if not addressed. I recognise the theme of the void in many of the stories and poems written in this book. It is hugely overwhelming for a child to understand and manage, but being able to express their feelings and reach out to others is the start of the healing process. This healing is integral to the survival of the people affected by these issues. Had books like this been available to me when I was young, I would have read these writings, been moved and comforted by them, but above all I would have felt less alone and perhaps have begun my healing process a lot earlier.

Rhona Cameron

Rhona Cameron is a comedian and author. Her first book was *1979: A big year in a small town* (Ebury, 2003). Described in *The Observer* as 'a candid open-hearted memoir', it tells the story of a 13-year-old Rhona coming to terms with her sexuality and losing her father. This was recently followed by a debut novel, *The Naked Drinking Club* (Ebury, 2008). Set in Sydney in the late '80s, this 'beautiful depiction of addiction and hedonism' traces a young woman's drunken search for her birth mother, while selling mass-produced paintings door to door.

Preface

Creating *The Colours in Me*

This collection brings together the writing, poetry, artwork and oral testimony of over 100 adopted children and young people who live or have lived in England, Ireland and Wales. Eighty-six individual children and young people, including a sibling group of three brothers, have contributed. In addition, there is a collective piece of writing from 23 young people aged 15–21 years who attended a conference for young adoptees.

The 86 children and young people were between four and 20 years old at the time of writing. They include adoptees who were adopted from the care system in the UK and transnational adoptees whose birth and heritage lie in another country. Over a third (30 out of 86) of the contributors are transnational adoptees. They were born in China (10), Guatemala (4), Romania (4), Thailand (3), Russia (2), Vietnam (2), Ethiopia (2), Bolivia (1), Bulgaria (1) and the Ukraine (1) and adopted by families living in England and Ireland. Children and young people with learning disabilities and physical and visual impairments are represented, to a lesser extent. The inclusion of artwork, photographs and oral testimony has enabled at least two children who can neither read nor write to be a part of this edited collection.

The project was publicised over roughly an 18-month period from January 2007 to June 2008. Adoption agencies in the statutory and voluntary sector in England, Scotland, Wales and Ireland were approached by email, as were regional adoption support agencies, adoptive parent support groups and listservs, particularly those for transnational adoptive parents. Individual social workers and adoptive parent groups for transnational adopters known to the editor were contacted. Additional publicity came through a range of service user and community groups including Shaping Our Lives National User Network, Adults Affected by Adoption-NORCAP and Adoption UK. Methods of publicity included postings on websites and online forums, articles in newsletters, talking with groups of social workers and adoptive parents, and attending a group event for adopted children.

More often than not, adoptive mothers and fathers made contact, with a small number of adoptees in their teens and older getting in touch directly by email. For a fifth of adoptees (17 out of 86), contact was solely or initially through a social worker, adoption team manager or publicity and recruitment worker in adoption. Thus, in the main, contact with children and young people was mediated through their parents and, to a lesser extent, social work professionals. Oral testimony was usually recorded in writing by adoptive parents. A telephone conversation with one young person, with the adoptee editing and adding to my write-up of our conversation, resulted in several contributions. Most submissions were sent by email, some by post and one was provided in person by an adoption social worker.

Understandably, some adoptive parents were cautious about the call for submissions and others suggested that their child/ren was too young or had not been with them long enough to contribute. Others did not hold any fears or concerns about what their child/ren might say about adoption or the feelings that writing may give rise to and their capacity to contain them. They encouraged and supported their child/ren to contribute, sometimes through writing down their child's oral testimony. (As expected, a small number of enquiries did not lead to any submissions being made.) Timing of the call for submissions and publication was crucial. Indeed, one adoptive mother withdrew her daughter's writing prior to publication which raises the ethical issue of consent. Another reported that the process of writing had not been straightforward or pain-free but had been very worthwhile. Many parents subsequently conveyed their child's joy and excitement in having their writing and/or artwork accepted for inclusion in this anthology.

Significantly, a large number of children have chosen to write under their first name, their initials or a pseudonym of their choice. There are obvious reasons for this, including the need to protect privacy as well as to ensure that their adoptive name and precise geographical location do not enter the public domain. The latter could make them easy to trace and there may, for some, be associated issues of safety relating to their pre-adoption history. In many instances, the names of other people (family members, foster carers, adoptive parents and social workers) mentioned in articles or poetry have been changed, as have references to specific towns or cities. In contrast, many transnational adoptees have chosen to include identifying information in their writing and biographical paragraph, and to write under their full adoptive and/or birth name.

As editor, I have tried to change only minimally the writing of each child or young person, altering spelling inaccuracies and occasionally the odd word, and adding in any missing words. More often that not, the sentence structure has not been altered at all. Some submissions have not been included, but only where the same child or young person has one or more other pieces of writing, poetry and/or artwork included. In addition, several written submissions have been omitted where they have not touched upon adoption, plus a poem by someone now an adult in her 50s.

Unfortunately, no submissions were received from adopted children and young people living in Scotland, despite contact with several Scotland-based individual workers and adoptive mothers. There are some other groups of adoptees who are not represented. These include children who were born in India (the third most popular "sending" country of children for adoption in England in 2007), children who have indicated that they are placed with a gay adoptive father(s) and young people where the adoptive placement has formally disrupted. These silences suggest submerged voices that need to be addressed in future work. Despite these limitations, this collection breaks new ground, being the first time that the words, artwork and oral testimony of adopted children and young people in England, Ireland and Wales have been brought together into one publication.

Listening to adopted children and young people's views and experiences

It is now recognised that instead of accepting adult representations and interpretations of children's lives, it is essential to convey children's own accounts of their views and experiences, first hand, so that we can develop our understanding by hearing from the children and young people themselves about what is important to them, how they construct their social world, and its meaning and significance for their lives. If we view adopted children and young people as competent and reflexive in reporting their own experiences, give them a voice and take what they say seriously, and parent or work for adopted children in ways that may benefit them (Mayall, 1996), it follows that adopted children and young people 'are likely to have their own concerns or questions' (Thomas and O'Kane, 2000, p 341). Indeed, research shows that children from a young age are able to give their views about a wide range of topics and that they want more say in their lives. The latter particularly applies to children who are 'looked after' or adopted (Thomas *et al*, 1999).

The Colours in Me sets out to hear first hand from adopted children and young people, so that we can develop our understanding of how they experience adoption, what is important to them and the meaning and significance of adoption in their lives. This collection tries to convey, in the words and art forms of adopted children and young people, their own views, experiences, memories, feelings and reflections on adoption.

In reading these poems, writings and artwork, we should view children as active participants in creating their adoption story, in creating meaning and in seeking to understand their respective adoption narrative. Each child will revisit their adoption story at different points in their childhood and adulthood, revising it and adding to it, as his or her understanding develops and new information is incorporated or obtained regarding the sequence of events, the involvement of other people and agencies, and the feelings and actions of others. In doing so, understandings may be developed and a fuller picture created. The latter includes an understanding of the role of poverty, environmental, economic and social factors in their adoption story, of the historical relationship between Britain and their specific country of origin (in the case of transnational adoptees), of the role of the state and the perspectives of social work and other professionals, of their adoptive parents' motivation to and journey to parenting by adoption, and of the perspectives of their birth mother, father, siblings and other birth relatives.

Thus, rather than view an adoption life story told by an adopted child or young person as somehow "incorrect" or "wrong", we need to read it as reflecting his or her experience of adoption and their current understanding. We need to remember that the official adoption story, the story in the adoption agency file or in agency documents, as with all knowledge, 'may be misleading or inaccurate and can only ever be partial at best given the complexity of real human lives' (Baynes, 2008, p 48). Any knowledge, including knowledge regarding a child's adoption, is partial or unfinished. Different perspectives will enhance it and provide a more rounded picture. Thus, the narrative or story of a child's adoption is never complete or finished and there will always be room to add to it.

Over time there will be shifts and developments in many children and young people's views and feelings about adoption. These will evolve, complementing, for most, their increasing capacity to understand and to express their thoughts, questions, concerns, loss and other emotions. Thus, the views and evaluations that a child may have regarding their experience may change from day to day and, almost certainly, over the years. By listening to children and how they understand and experience their adoption today, we will be in a better position to help and support them, whether as parents, family members, social workers, therapists or other professionals.

For the children and young people who have contributed to this book, sharing their adoption experiences through poetry, artwork, oral testimony and writing is an act of empowerment (Collins, 1990) demonstrating their ability to think and speak for themselves about the experience of adoption. This is an opportunity which we, as parents, adopted people, family members, social workers, adoption support social workers and other professionals, can offer to other adopted children and young people with whom we have contact. By helping children to create a coherent narrative of their life story, bringing together significant events and memories, feelings and thoughts, we can help each child to find meaning and understanding. We can increase our awareness of how adoption is being experienced by this particular child and begin to discern the world from this child's point of view.

Parents and social workers are strongly encouraged to draw upon this book to help adopted children to explore and voice their own thoughts, memories, experiences, feelings and questions about their respective adoption life story and adoption, in general. When doing so, we must be sensitive to the child and ready to respond to the feelings, emotions and questions that may arise for him or her. We can invite children to choose some aspect of their adoption experience or life story to write about or draw. We can invite them to write down the questions they have about adoption and any they might have about their birth family. We can invite children to write a letter to a birth relative or adoptive parent telling him or her whatever they would like to say. We can suggest they write and draw their own book about adoption. The list goes on. For those who may struggle to write or prefer to talk, we can be their scribe, the conduit for their expressions, or we can give them a camera or art materials to create and portray what adoption means to them. Writing and artwork are powerful media for the exploration of meaning and understanding. As one adoptive mother wrote regarding her daughter's submission:

> It was amazing to have this opportunity to be her pen and I wish to thank you for it as I would not have thought of doing this ourselves – it has taken us to a new level and she wishes to continue to write over time.

Structure

The book is divided into six sections. I have chosen not to introduce individual items as each piece of artwork, poetry or writing speaks more powerfully for itself. There are over-arching themes in each section and cross-cutting themes that readers will want to look out for. The first two sections are longer than the others, reflecting the topics that contributors chose to write, draw or speak about. A number of children and young people have contributed several pieces of writing and/or artwork; these are often spread throughout the book. A small number of pieces of artwork and writing were written or created in the past; the vast majority were developed specifically for this collection. Where the child or young person was a younger age at the time of writing, this age is given. You will see both similarities and differences between the ways the children and young people have written about, drawn about and understand their adoption.

The first section, **Adoption stories**, focuses on adoption life stories. Here adopted children and young people tell us about their memories of living with their birth family, in foster care, in institutional care and then moving to their adoptive family. For example, they speak of neglect, physical abuse, alcohol and drug misuse, and death in their birth family. They write about their feelings: sadness, fear, anger, excitement and happiness. Highlighting the positive difference that being adopted has made to their lives, they write and draw about life with their adoptive family.

The second section, **On being adopted**, brings together reflections on adoption that offer us insight into the lived experience of adoption and the meaning of adoption for adopted children and young people. This section encapsulates joy and happiness, loneliness and fear, confusion and anger, sadness and grief. It conveys children's questions and concerns including their continued thoughts and feelings about their birth family. "On being adopted" communicates both the ordinariness of everyday life and feelings of being different from other children. A range of issues are mentioned including experiencing racism, being bullied, placing siblings together, being told one is adopted and having contact with other adopted, black or minority ethnic children. Many children and young people write about their feelings about their adoptive family, expressing love for their adoptive parents and feeling loved by them.

Section 3, **On being apart**, focuses on feelings and thoughts about the loss of the mother who gave birth to them and other birth relatives. Here the longing, the unanswered questions, and the loss and grief stand raw. Writing, poetry and artwork that touch upon this theme can be found elsewhere too.

In the fourth section, **Staying in touch**, contributors write about their experiences of and feelings about staying in contact with a range of birth family members through visits, letters and telephone calls. One child, Sola, also writes and draws about her feelings about no longer seeing her sister who is adopted by a separate adoptive family, which contrasts starkly with Julia's poems about her ongoing letter contact with her sister. None of the contributors in this section are transnational adoptees.

The fifth section, **Revisiting my birth place**, focuses on experiences, meanings and feelings about visiting place of birth and country of origin; these range from London, England to China, Guatemala, Romania, Thailand and Vietnam. Nearly all the contributions are by transnational adoptees. They reveal the impact on children of visiting their place or country of birth. The section includes several pieces on meeting birth family members for the first time when visiting the adoptee's country of birth.

The final section, **Messages**, provides an array of perceptive messages primarily for adopted children and young people, although there are also important messages intended for adoptive parents and prospective adoptive parents, social workers, teachers and psychotherapists.

Background information on each child or young person, including photographs of many, is presented and the book closes with a list of useful websites.

The salience of what adopted children and young people are able to tell us about their memories, experiences, thoughts, understandings, questions and feelings – the colours in them – cannot be overestimated. Within these pages, the complexity of the child and young person's lived experience of adoption is laid bare. We are privileged to have this opportunity to enter into their world. Their words and artwork may not always make for easy reading, especially where their sorrow and pain are so stark. However, I hope you will find this collection invaluable and illuminating. These children's and young people's words and artwork are precious gems full of wisdom and insight which, taken together, may guide us all in our thinking and actions whatever our personal and/or professional connection to adoption. Listen to them and hear what they have to say.

For adopted children and young people reading this collection, I hope you will be able to identify with some of the stories, poems and artwork, and may be encouraged and inspired to write or draw about your own adoption experience. I hope you will feel able to share with a parent, family member, close friend or social worker some of your own feelings and thoughts about adoption. At the very least, my wish is that you will see that you are not alone in being adopted and that your experiences, feelings, questions and dreams for the future are shared with many others. This book is for you.

References

Baynes P (2008) 'Untold stories: a discussion of life story work', *Adoption & Fostering*, 32:1, pp 43–49

Collins P H (1990) *Black Feminist Thought: Knowledge, consciousness and the politics of empowerment*, London: Routledge

Mayall B (1996) *Children, Health and the Social Order*, Buckingham: Open University Press

Thomas C and Beckford V, with Lowe N and Murch M (1999) *Adopted Children Speaking*, London: BAAF

Thomas N and O'Kane C (2000) 'Discovering what children think: connections between research and practice', *British Journal of Social Work*, 30, pp 819–35

SECTION 1

Adoption stories

Sophie's story

Sophie (age 6)

I feel excited because I'm adopted now,
do you want to know my story, how?

I was sad when I didn't have a proper mum and dad,
and that made me feel quite sad.

When I met my new mum and dad I was happy,
because I knew they'd be nice to me.

I like that my mum and dad keep my house clean,
they take me places and they're not mean.

I like the things I do,
like bike rides, swimming and the zoo!

We go on holiday to the seaside,
and at the park there are lots of rides.

I am pleased that life has changed for me,
now that I'm with my family.

I know we will stay a family together,
and I will be loved forever.

Impressions of my early days

Conor Henry (age 6)

When I was born I was very small so I was put into an incubator in the hospital. Then I went to the baby home near Bangkok. There were lots of other babies there. One day two *tuk tuks* and a bendy bus came and brought us all to Siam Ocean World Aquarium. We saw sting rays, jelly fish (my favourites), stone fish and an octopus. Then Mama and Dada came to the baby home and took me away. We went on an aeroplane. It was a very long journey. Now I live in Ireland with my family. I have a sister. She is from Thailand too.

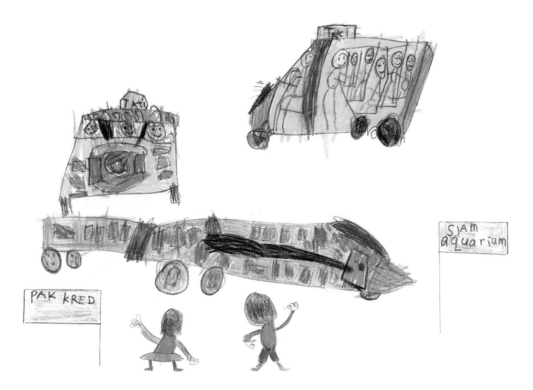

Conor's great adventure

It's all about understanding my family

Millie (age 10)

Adoption is how you move family and have a happy new life. You start your life again with a new family. My mum couldn't look after me or my sister or my brother. She never learned how – she was very young then. We had to move to a different family to be looked after for a bit while they found me and my sister and brother a new family. It was very sad to leave my mum. I didn't want to leave her. I was very young then and didn't understand. I didn't want to go. My foster family were nice. They had a dog and a turtle that I used to like. Now that dog is dead and I miss her. I only had one Christmas there until I got a real family to live with for the rest of my life. My brother was separated from us. It's a shame that he had to move. He was very young and my foster mum couldn't handle him because he was screaming mad. We didn't go to visit him a lot. Now I go and see him with my new family. And sometimes he comes to stay with us with his new family.

Someone from social services told me that I'm having a new family with my sister. The first day I met them I opened the door and ran to them because I was so happy that I had a new mum and dad. While my sister was at school my new mum and dad would collect me from playschool. We once went to a park behind the playschool and I hurt myself. I fell off something – the pole like a fireman has.

I went to live with my new family who had a squash and squeeze house. It was so squashed. It was a very small house but it was nice and I didn't mind. I thought it was nice and I loved my bedroom. Me and my sister shared a bedroom at the back. We had a chalkboard and shelves and all our toys and we played there. I used to creep to my mum and dad's room in the morning and wait outside their door and wait for them to come out and get me. They would carry me into their bed. I just loved to do that. It made me feel nice. I feel happy now and I like it.

Sometimes I feel sadness for my mum and wish that I was with her. I write to my mum every summer and she writes back to me and she gives me birthday cards. When I think about her I think that I am happy in my new family and that I love her and I will never forget her. When I'm 18 it will be nice that I can see her again. When I am 18 I might go with my sister or my mum or my dad or all of them to see her. I would bring some clothes with me and I might stay there. Not forever – to visit. One thing that sometimes makes me sad is when my friends ask me about my mum – what she looks like and why she wasn't able to look after me. I explain that I don't want to talk about it because it's a private thing and it makes me feel sad.

I got a happy and fun family now. The best thing is that they bring me on holidays to different countries and we get to see what the different money looks like and stuff. I feel happy, happy, happy and good to be here.

I might live close by my mum when I grow up. I might work in England. Or I might have my mum and dad's house. I'm actually not sure if I'll take their house. They might need it when they're old.

Adopted

Lex Wolf (age 20)

So far as I recall it, there I was one night watching TV and being slapped behind the head if I was falling asleep.

Days past and I was wishing for and thinking of a better life.

Doing and being at the same place got boring.

A few days later a group of volunteers came to help out at the home.

Among them was a short-haired woman who stood out.

She had red cheeks and a kind face. Her voice was soft and kind that it made me feel safe and secure inside.

She came to visit the home and went back to England. A few months past and she would come again.

I'd remember who she was straight away. I'd miss her and tell the other kids that she was my mum.

As time went on, I was wishing for one thing and that was for her to be my mum. Her name was Della and she was so kind and understanding with all the kids that she worked with.

Every time she left to go back to England, I was very sad and disappointed that she didn't take me with her.

I was sad and lonely; when she was there she made me feel like I was someone, not just a kid in a kids' home.

Years passed and we were walking hand-in-hand to the ticket line in the airport.

She had done it, she adopted me and was going to take me to England. The plane took off…

And we were at Gatwick Airport where her mother lives. When we got to the door a very big dog greeted me and started to lick me and speak doggie language to me. I was very happy to be there.

And I am still very happy, happy that my life has got better, and all this because I was adopted by someone who cares.

To be here with my new family is more than I can ask for, they are so understanding and kind to me, that's why I am more than grateful to my mum who is such a great, kind and loving woman, who adopted me by herself, with hard work and time.

She was and has been the one and only person I'd like to be my mum. Without her I would not have a life or, at least, not like I do now. Here I am with an education and clothes and money, a mind and a soul.

She has made me into what I am today and I thank her very much.

My mum was there for me through thick and thin, that's why I love her so much.

I am grateful for what she has accomplished. Thanks Mum, I love you very much.

It's sad, it's happy ... it's my life

Georgie (age 11)

My life started out in not a fair way. Our house was a tip. It was very cold – it had no heating and it had hardly anything in it. I was often hungry and remember vividly helping my little sister up on the counter to make ourselves a jam sandwich. I used to think, 'I have to grow up now and make myself something to eat because my mum is asleep and I am all alone in life.' I used to act like the mother to my sister and brother because my mum wasn't able to. Once I remember my mum cooking chips and it burst into flames because she had fallen asleep and I had to wake her up. I was too young to really understand but I felt worried. Because my life was like that I had no idea what it would be like to have a warm and cosy home and a proper mum and all that. My mum was too busy worrying about her own problems. She had a lot of problems and it wasn't her fault. She was never mean to us.

One day a lady took us in her car and brought us to our foster parents' house. I had no idea where I was going. My little sister and little brother were sitting in the back screaming their heads off. I was in a car with a complete stranger who I didn't know was a social worker. I was four-and-a-half years old. The lady gave us lollies to calm us down. I wasn't crying but I was upset that my brother and sister were crying. I felt so bad. The lady didn't say anything to us. When I arrived at my foster parents' house I remember the holly wreath on the door – it was close to Christmas. The house looked warm and welcoming and I was happy to go in. The rest of my memory of this is blank.

That was the year I got my favourite toy. It was a doll and although she wasn't a fancy or posh doll I adored her and I treasure her still, even though her eye has gone crooked and she is old. I love her because she reminds me of how my new life started out. I am so happy to have her because she reminds me of how happy I was to get her.

I loved my foster parents' house. They had loads of pets. They brought us to school and fed us well. It felt very nice. I was too happy in that house to worry about my other life. One day I heard screaming and yelling in the hallway. A lady gave me a cat bag and gave my sister a dog bag. She gave my brother a colourful rucksack. Then she took my brother away. I didn't know where he was going – I thought he was just going out. I can't remember anyone explaining this to me.

My brother was separated from us and now he is living in another country with his new parents.

Later my foster mother explained that we would be moving to a new family. I took all this adoption scenario in a very easy way. I knew I'd be moving family because my social worker had told me. And I thought about it as 'great – I'm going to a lovely new family and a cosy home and lovely new toys and things'. I didn't know who my family would be at that time but I liked to think about what they might be like. When I met my new parents I was glad because they were a teeny bit nervous too. They weren't jumping in on me and giving me hugs like they had known me for a long time because that would just be scary.

At the time when I went to my new family I didn't like myself for some reason. I used to punch myself and sulk to get attention. I hated myself. My new mum and dad kept giving me attention and happily, gradually I started to like myself. My mum and dad used to sit with me, chat to me, scratch my back and soothe me. My mum used to lie in my bed with me and chat to me.

I am very ultra happy now. I try my best at school and love it. I want to work as a social worker when I grow up because with my experience I think I'd be quite successful.

When I think of my mum now I feel like she is someone I know at the edge of my mind. Like a cousin. I forget what she used to look like although she sends me photos. She is like a faded memory floating away. In the future I picture and wish that when I am in my 20s I will be in nice clothes going to visit my mum, with cakes in my hands. We would be chatting and laughing and acting like good friends. One thing I miss is not having had the chance to be a baby. When I see people giving loads of attention to babies I feel upset that I never had that chance and I never will.

I don't want my life to change ever again. I don't want to have to move again. I never will. I love my parents so much I could die with love for them. I have a really strong feeling for them and they are naturals at being parents. I would do anything in the world for them and I cry in bed sometimes when I think of something bad happening to them.

A child's tale

Holly Brooksbank (age 19)

I'm 19 years old and I have been adopted for 13 years now, but before I talk about my new life I want to tell you a bit about the life I lived before I was adopted.

A few months after I was born my mother decided to put me into care, just for a while so she could sort her life out as she was a single teenage mother. I can imagine she was finding life a bit difficult as she was only 18 and had two children, and no man around to help her. Anyway I kept going back and forth to foster placements. I was with a foster family who I lived with for a couple of years. I enjoyed this placement a lot and I was angry when I had to go back and live with my mother and her new boyfriend. I was four years old at this point and had only been living with my mother and her boyfriend for a few months. While I and my sister had been at the foster placement, my mother had had two more children who belonged to her new boyfriend. My sister had recently started school and I and my stepbrothers were too young to go to playschool so we just stayed at home with my mother's boyfriend. He was a nasty, nasty man who treated me very badly and made my life hell. I'll give you a little example without too much graphics. He used to take my toys and destroy them, chew up my jewellery that other people brought me. And then there was the violence. I won't describe this to you or give you examples as it is not very nice. But even now, 14 years later, I can still remember everything about my past life, the good memories and the bad, the house I used to live in, the room I used to sleep in, the fear I felt every minute of every day and night.

The story ends well though. I was then taken away from my mother and her horrible boyfriend and placed into a foster home which I loved very much. They made me feel so special and welcome. I have a lot of lovely memories of this foster placement that will stay in my heart forever. A few years later my social worker came to see me at my foster home and told me she had found me a permanent home where I could live until I was old enough to move out. Well 13 years down the line, I'm still living with my adoptive parents. They're the best parents anyone could ask for. As far as I'm concerned they are and always will be my parents.

About my life

Jade (age 10)

When I lived with my birth family I was only 0–3 years old. I remember being with my mum's boyfriend and his sister Sally but that is really how much I remember. I still think about my mum today. She died when I was just turned three. I was sad from that day onwards.

The first time I went into foster care was when I was 15 months old because my mum was on drugs at that time and could not stop or care for me. I was very confused at the time. I was only a baby. Then I went back to my mum because she sorted herself out and could control herself. When my mum died, I had to go back into foster care because I had no one to care for me but for a little while I stayed with a lady named Helen. Then in came my dad. I lived with him for a year but he could not look after me any more. So I went to a family for a while but then I moved on to my foster family. I stayed there for two-and-a-half years. I loved it there. It was like it was home forever. One time when I used to go and see my dad he gave me sweets and I used to irritate Josh, who is my foster brother. I used to wave them in his face. Another time, me and Millie spied on Tim. When he went to the toilet we hid in the cupboard in the bathroom.

When I was with my foster family, I saw a therapist called Rebecca. I saw her every week at a centre. One day she brought a little booklet. I was very eager to see what it was about, so she told me to open it. My foster carer Caroline read it to us. It said, 'Jade, someone wants to adopt you' and when I turned the page there was a beautiful picture of my new mum. I was over the moon about getting a new mum. I was allowed to call her 'Mum' but her real name is Rose. She was going to be my new real mum. A couple of weeks later Rose called and told my foster carer where I was going to live; she said I was going to live in London. I was happy and sad. The reason I was happy was because I got to live in London. The reason I was sad was because it was far from where I was living now, but at least I could come and visit everyone in the holidays. I knew what adoption was. Caroline explained that I would not always live with her that I would move on and find a real mum that would always be there for me.

Well, I was waiting for a very long time to get adopted and I could not wait to get adopted. It meant the world to me that I was going to have a mum that I could call 'Mum' and not have to call her by her first name. I knew that I was going to be in the adoption newspaper but when I found out I had a mum I did not know that they had put me in it already! I was very joyful when Caroline told me that I was up for adoption. I wanted a family with other older children but it ended up that I did not get a brother or a sister, I just got a mum but I was still overjoyed about this big drama that was happening.

I was helped to pack. I knew when I was moving and what day I would be going. We got a lot of cardboard boxes for all my toys and books. It felt a bit strange moving my stuff again. It was another big journey that I was going on. A couple of days later I was about to meet my new mum for the first time! I felt like a total bag of nerves to meet my new and true mum. That day when I was at school, I drew a picture for her to say that I already loved her. The day I met her all my friends and teachers wished me the best of luck, that this was the right mum for me, they just knew it in their blood. I came into the room with my foster sister and there was my new mum, Rose, sitting on the comfy sofa. She had made herself at home in seconds. We talked about what we would do in London, like go on the London Eye, see the Houses of Parliament and, most importantly, Big Ben.

We met a couple of times. The second day was the weekend so we went shopping in town. We went to Woolworths, Roy's, Stead and Simpson's and the grocery store to get some strawberries and oranges. The third day we took Rose to our church. She really liked our church. She said it was much bigger than her church. The night before we left to go to London for the first time I had my mum's car keys. I opened her boot and threw the keys in the back of her boot and slammed the door shut. The reason I put the keys in the boot was because I did not want to leave. The next day Rose asked me if I knew where her keys had gone and I said nothing. I ran upstairs as fast as my legs could go. She called the AA and they came and we were off in no time. I cried a river of tears; that was how much I did not want to leave!

The best things about being adopted though is that you get to go to adoption parties, meet new people and children and go out to places for a couple of nights. When I went to Peterborough camping everyone was adopted, we collected wood from the dusty forest and gathered around the campfire.

We have also been to France with our local adoption group. That was amazing. We spoke in French. We ate French food. It was delightful.

But the worst thing about being adopted is everyone wants to know what happened, what it feels like and they always say, 'I feel sorry for you', and go all soppy. I was very sad when I had to change schools because I had made loads of new friends and then I was moved. I was really upset because I had to leave my best friend behind called Cameron but I stay in contact with her. But I moved to a very good school. I had friends in no time. My best friend is Alanna. She came in Year 5.

Well, my name is Jade. I am from Essex. I am ten-and-a-half. I live in London. I'm in my last year at primary which is Year 6. I love animals. I have a dog and a hamster and might get a rabbit. I like loads about myself. I am a world traveller. I have been to New Zealand, Africa-Tanzania, Scotland, New York and France.

I feel really happy when it is Christmas because you get loads of nice presents and you celebrate Jesus's birthday. I also feel super happy when it is my birthday because I get to be a new number, like next year I am going to be 11 years old. I feel a bit sad when it's Mother's Day because I never made my mum a card but this year I did and I put it in my small garden so she could see it, from heaven.

The thing about my family is they are from different countries but my adopted family are just from England. My nan is from Ireland. My granddad is from Pakistan and I do not know where my dad is from.

Bottom of a bottle

Francis Davies (at age 16)

From whenever it is that my very first memory is, it's of me being a very smiley, content and all-round happy kid. Mum and me went places and did things together; always together. I was very happy. I had everything I wanted and it all seemed great. The few minor upsets, like sitting on a wasp and getting stung, were miniscule specks of black upon a clear white background of my early years, on this seemingly innocent, good natured and nice little life of mine.

Yeah. I had everything – all the toys, my family that looked after me and places I could go. My first bike that I rode into a park gate and well near brained myself on. My big brother's lead soldiers that they would never let me touch in case I started sucking on one and received lead poisoning from the well-crafted metal monsters that always looked so good, and captivated my imagination and attention every time I was in my sister's father's house.

I would sit in our two-bedroom flat and play with the batman and the various other toys I had for ages, most of the day. Just let me go and off I went. And I would go for the whole day. I was fine like that.

Mum would seem to bring random guys home sometimes. At the time I didn't fully understand this, only the feeling that they would stay for a while. Well, of course, now I know that she was after another guy to replace my father after he ran away. She went in and out of relationships with several people. People that I never quite felt were particularly good people. Didn't know why at the time, but now I guess that somewhere in my childish mind I could sense that they were just like my mother. Addicted to alcohol and getting drunk on it. Like her they stared into empty cans and bottles, trying to get the very last drops into their alcohol infested blood.

The only difference was that my mother had tried her best to stop, stop for me. But in the end I guess she found it just that bit too hard to stop drinking herself into stupors. The alcohol was too deeply ingrained in her and eventually she went down, taking me with her.

It's strange how I can still remember the three promises she gave me when I was growing up. Still a toddler about three years old, but I still remember:

'I promise you I will always look after you,

I will always care and I will never hit you.'

She broke all three. With the days and nights of continuous drinking and sleeping, the small lapses in between, where she would stagger around drunkenly looking for another can, she broke every promise she made to me. I can still remember vividly the time I spent alone in that flat whilst she slept for another day or two. I can remember it all too well.

It was sunny, I was in the front room playing with the batmobile I had received last Christmas only a few months previous. She came in and told me we were going up the road. I put on my shoes and coat and off we went to the top of the hill, where a row of shops stood overlooking the road. I thought we would go into the post office. It was the only shop we had ever been in, out of all the shops on that small strip of pavement. Instead I was dragged past it. Immediately I was very confused. Where was mum going?

We turned into a small shop. There were row upon row of shelves. All filled to the brim with all sorts of cans – gold, blue, black. I grew all the more puzzled as to why we were in here instead of the post office. She walked quickly over to six cans held together with some sort of thin semi-clear plastic. Lifted them up and took them to the counter.

Suddenly I was on edge. A small flare of imminent danger and warning blared in my infantile mind. I didn't like this shop with its dingy, crowded looking cans and shelves. I wanted out. We went out, back into the sunlight of the early spring morning. Suddenly the sunlight didn't look so pleasing and neither did the clear blue sky, which held it. All I could think was that those cans were bad news.

We walked back to the tall, dirty block of flats. It's crazy, but until then I had never noticed how run down and bad the place looked. It was only through the buying of those cans that I started to notice the small pockets of darkness. And suddenly my nice clean background had many more dots of black on it.

We got back in and I watched Mum set the cans down on the floor. All except one. Once more the warning went off in the back of my head. I didn't want to see those cans any more, so I went into the front room to play. In fact I was scared of those golden cans. Not like the fear after a nightmare or the fear that a monster was going to lurch into my room and devour me, after watching one too many horror themed cartoons. This was like a wake-up call. It signalled that real fear like nothing I had ever experienced was about to open its eyes and grip me with its terrifying gaze. This fear was terrible and deep. It went right through me and sucked out the happiness. Even my toys could not distract me. I couldn't drive away the thought of my mother standing there with a long gold can clutched in her hand.

I went out into the hallway to go to my room. The cans were not there. More fear swept through me. I decided to seek out the cans. I looked into my mum's room. There she was lying on her bed sprawled like a shot bird. Around her crumpled form were six cans, open and laying side on. This time no panic or fear swept through me. She was sleeping. It was fine. There was nothing wrong; she must have simply been thirsty. With the thoughts of normality softly blocking out the fear that had constricted on me only moments before, I returned to the front room and the TV, totally unaware that there was no more normality. No more everyday. Totally unknowing that my small world was about to go from peaceful and filled to empty and chaotic.

These words seem like a complete contradiction and seemingly make no sense at all, but that's what it was like. Over the weeks I spent alone, with myself and a woman who only got up to buy some more beer and drink herself back into a coma that would last from one to three days, I did realise that something was wrong with her. I also realised there was nothing I could do. So I did what I could for myself. I got drinks by climbing onto the kitchen table and pouring the contents of a bottle into a dirty glass, which I used repeatedly. I could get nothing to eat as food was in the fridge and the handle was out of reach. So I would wait for my mother to resurface, still drunk, stagger from her room and bring me a plate of cheese and crackers every few days, if she remembered.

By now she had broken two of her promises. 'Looking after me' and 'caring' had been washed from her lips by the alcohol running out of her mouth, as she drank herself past consciousness. At about the one-month mark she broke the third, 'I will never hit you.' I was on my way to the kitchen; it was about noon and I was in the hall. She appeared in front of me and I looked up at her with a happy smile, pleased that she had raised herself after the three-day sleep. She looked down at me with an unknowing, blank, intoxicated stare. She grabbed me and started hitting me.

I had no idea why and nor did I care. She had just broken her last promise. The hitting faded into the background as the emotional realisation hit me. It hit me harder than anything I have ever felt. I was crushed completely. That was the last shard of hope I had clung to, the last thread that might have symbolised an end to what was happening. She snapped it. She tore it in two like a dirty rag and threw it away. I broke away and ran to my room and sat there motionless against the door. I felt empty, angry, confused and broken. She had shattered my hope. There was no coming back from this. She didn't care. She didn't want to. She was wrapped up in the alcohol and there was no space for anything else.

For the next month I did what I had done before: carried on as usual. But there was a difference. This time everything lacked its previous enjoyment and spirit; there was no drive in it and no happiness, just a gaping empty pit where my happiness used to be. I played quietly without expression, my face blank with staring empty eyes. When I watched TV I didn't laugh or find it entertaining. I watched it because I could do nothing else. My plain white background was now completely black. I'm unclear how long I went on like this. It's blurry and confused.

I was sitting watching TV, the same emptiness and the same pain. The same confusion, the same fear and the same anger all surrounding me and enveloping me like a blanket, crushing out everything good. Still I sat there unmoving, not laughing, uncaring. Nothing seems to matter anymore. My mum didn't care, there was nothing to eat and all that was left was a cold empty shell of the child I once was.

I was sitting there like that when there was a loud thump on the door. Danger. My first instinct was danger. I chose the first suitably sheltering thing I could see to hide in: the table. So I crouched under the table, scared and wondering what was happening. And my mother appeared, staggering over to the door and opening it. I went and stood behind her. People. Two people. They towered above me and started talking to what was my mother. One of them asked me to take one thing with me, so I went into my room and on the end of my bed was the stuffed toy I had had since I was first born. I picked it up and made to leave. She stopped me.

'Don't you want this one too?' she asked, waving another that I had grown quite attached to, but seemed a lot less meaningful. I nodded and my mother looked at them with pleading eyes. They nodded and I was taken out onto the balcony into the night, down the foul-looking stairs and put into a car. I sat in the back and as the car started I took one look back at the towering flats looming in the dark night sky. The car started moving and I turned away with only the thought that I knew I would never see the place I had called home again. Neither would I see the person I called mum and the thing I called life…

This event changed me catastrophically. A large part of my happiness and stability was torn out because of this; I'm left with scars and a lot of personal pain and anger. However, for all the pain, the anger, insecurity and everything else it left me, I feel stronger for it. This gave me a determination and strength to take everything else that was thrown at me after that, and even things that will be coming my way in future. I guess it could be described with the phrase 'Whatever doesn't kill you makes you stronger'.

I'm also a lot more aware of how badly drink can mess up your life and the lives of people around you. Things like this always have shockwaves that will destroy whatever isn't directly affected by someone's mess. Although I was the most affected, I wasn't the only one to be damaged by her addiction.

I don't think I will ever get over that. I will always have that with me, as much as I could try to put it in the back of my mind and forget about it, it's always going to be there and it's always going to hurt. So I can try and live with it, despite everything it has given me.

My "pop-up" story

Smurfy (age 15)

In 2006, I read in the adoption agency magazine that there was going to be a competition, to produce something to help young people waiting to be adopted. I thought that I would like to enter. I was 13 at the time. I decided that my entry should be for five to seven- or eight-year-olds, therefore, I thought the idea of poetry or a leaflet wouldn't really appeal to that age group. So I sat down and thought long and hard. I eventually came up with the idea of a children's pop-up book, with "fun things" to do in it, like open the curtains, etc. There are lots of "fun" elements in the book (well, fun for younger children), such as curtains that open and close, a door that opens and closes and push-up, pop-up pages. I thought it would give information and hope to young children who are waiting to be adopted.

The book tells the story of a young girl called Amy, who lives with her brother and sister. They aren't very nice to her. One day the doorbell rings and Amy's sister, Carrie, tells Amy to open the door. When she opens it, she sees a social worker standing on the doorstep. The social worker sees that Amy isn't very happy and she asks if Amy enjoys living with her brother and sister. Amy says that she doesn't much enjoy it. So with the social worker's help, she moves out of her house and into a foster family. From there, the social workers and her foster parents, Barbie and Ken, help her to find a "new family". She is going to be adopted. There is a happy ending; everyone lives happily ever after!

The story is not based on anything from my own experience or anyone I know. I used to watch *Tracy Beaker* on TV (a programme about a girl who used to live with her family, but went into care at the age of eight; it tells the story of her and her friends). I remember that one of the children in the programme lived with his brother for a while, so I kind of adapted it to my story and changed bits, e.g. Amy didn't go to a care home, she went to a foster family.

I think I would have liked a book, or something information-wise, when I came into care, but I was nine at the time so maybe this book would have been a little too young. Something similar, but more age appropriate would have been very helpful. Mainly to let me know that there was light at the end of the tunnel!

I won the competition for my age group!

Here are two pages from my book.

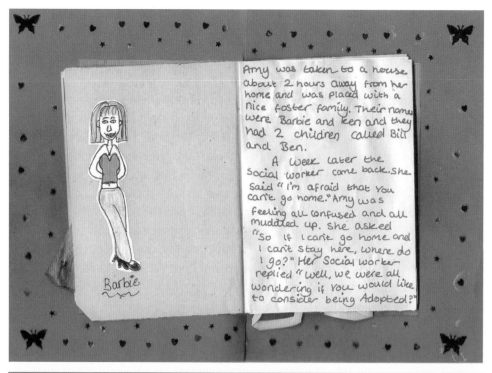

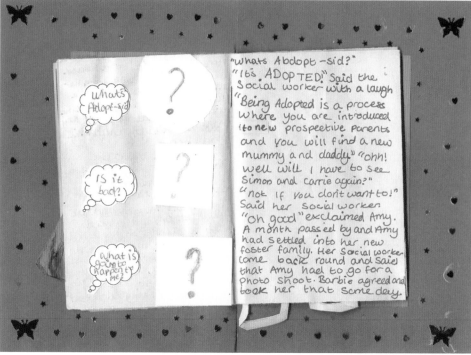

Adoption day

James (at age 11)

My family always celebrates October 16. Why? It's not my birthday, it's not Christmas, but it is the day when two years ago I went to the High Court of Justice in the Strand with my family.

What was I going to court for? I was ten, so I was old enough to get a criminal record. What had I done? Had I murdered someone? No! Had I done criminal damage? No!

It was my adoption hearing.

I was dressed very smartly in new clothes. My younger brother Anthony was with us. My teenage brothers Jack and Stephen came and they were dressed very smartly too.

It was the first time I had seen Stephen without a hooded sweatshirt. They moaned because they were told to take off their baseball caps to go into court.

I had to go into court where there was a woman judge sitting in an enormous chair by a big desk. A man banged on the table with a hammer and said, 'Silence in court'. Then the judge asked my mum and dad if they wanted to adopt me and my brother. They replied, 'Yes we do'. Then they asked my social worker Louise if we were happy in our new family. She commented that we were very happy and were doing well at school. Then she asked me. I felt nervous but I said I wanted to stay with my new family. She asked Anthony what he wanted to do and he said stay. Then the judge said, 'I will write in my book that today Anthony and James became members of the Smith family'.

We went out of the court and my mum and dad gave us all new signet rings with our new initials on. It was a bit like having a wedding ring. My mum took a photograph of all her four sons showing their rings off. Then our old social worker Louise said goodbye to us – it was the first time in my life that I had not had a social worker.

Afterwards my family and two of our friends, Tracy and Natasha, came out for a meal with us. Then we went to the Trocodero and went on the dodgems. We had lots of fun and it felt even better because I should have been at school.

The next day I had another half-day off school. There was a special lunch for children who had been adopted. Guess where it was? It was in the Houses of Parliament. We had to go with our special invitations to the entrance to the House of Lords; it was the same entrance that the Queen uses. The children had a party with a clown while the adults listened to boring speeches. Then we went out to the balcony by the river and had lots of coke and cakes. I had my picture taken in the Houses of Parliament. It was good fun being there and I met some other children who had been adopted. So, now you know why my family always celebrates October 16. This year we have tickets for the circus. We get to celebrate another adoption day in March which is when my brothers were adopted ten years ago.

My adoption experience

Marcus Wootton-Kahn (age 20)

My name is Marcus and I'm 20 years old, and adopted, and I have a learning difficulty. I came into care at the age of eight years old. I spent one week with an emergency foster carer called Margee before I came to my other foster carer, Helen, when I was eight years old. When I first came to Helen I felt a little bit scared at first and I didn't know what to expect. Then it got much better. I felt safe and loved and went to lots of places with my friends and my foster mum.

At 15 years old I wanted Helen to adopt me but social workers wouldn't listen to me. They kept asking me, what is the difference between fostering and adoption? They said that they are both the same thing. I felt that social workers wanted to stop me from being adopted so I left it for a while. Then one of my best friends convinced me that adoption was a very good thing. Helen rang Peter who used to be my guardian. Peter gave Helen the name of a very good solicitor and applied to adopt me. I wrote to the judge saying what I wanted. I always knew what adoption meant. I told people that my foster mummy would be my mummy by law. I did get adopted on the 5th of November 2003 when I was 16 years old. My adoption treat was to stay at the luxury Alton Towers Hotel all over the Christmas holiday. I am now 20 years old and I'm very happy and doing very well at college.

When I was a baby adopted in China

Harriet Cox (age 5)

Sadness and happiness

Ayesha (age 10)

It all started with sadness. The stray puppy Tommy was looking at his only family left, his mother lying on the floor in pain. She was terribly ill and really wanted someone to look after her loving son Tommy. With her only strength left she dragged Tommy carefully to the fostering centre. Tommy was really scared and confused what his mother Rose was going to do with him.

Rose filled in some forms and with teardrops falling from her loving eyes she got taken away to the hospital without a chance to say goodbye to Tommy. After that Tommy was driven to a foster home and as soon as he stepped through the door he saw lots and lots of children screaming, shouting, playing games, watching TV. It was unbelievable. Tommy had never seen as much madness as this before.

Tommy needed a friend, someone for him to care for and them to care for him. Then he noticed something. There was a sad little kitten weeping on the bottom of the stairs. He moved slowly towards her and in a very soft voice he said, 'Hello, my name is Tommy. You can call me Tom if you want.' She looked up at him and said, 'Hi, I am Lilly,' then they both started talking about how they got to the fostering home.

Weeks went on until one day, while Lilly and Tommy were playing hide and seek, Tommy received some news. His mother wanted to see her son so he had to go to the hospital. Tommy went up to Lilly and said, 'Please come and see my mum with me. She would love you.' Lilly said yes because Tommy was her best friend.

When they arrived Tommy spotted his mum and ran straight to her. While he got closer he saw lots of tubes and things on his mum. She wasn't any better than before. That made Tommy anxious. He thought his mum would die, but that's not what she wanted to talk to him about. She said that she will be too ill to look after him and she said she wants him to have a family who has a home who will feed you, someone who would keep you fit, healthy and love you for the rest of their lives.

That did happen. Tommy got adopted by lovely caring parents but that's not all. He got a sister as well. Guess who that was? It was Lilly. Tommy and Lilly both visited their birth parents at the weekend and they both lived happily ever after.

The End

By the sea

Harriet (age 11)

The seaside is fun, believe me it is! I love the sea; I once spent four hours in the sea. I have lived in eleven foster homes, in the last one I was at the seaside. We went on the beach with Jenny [the foster carer] and we have had a letter to say we can go on a picnic with her. With my mum and dad I go to the seaside twice a year. You go on more holidays when you're adopted.

My life

Marina Harris (age 12)

I can't exactly remember how old I was but this is what I was told when I was little: my parents couldn't cope with all their children and could not afford it. My mum had four other kids at the time including me, five. I was one of the newest members of the family. My dad had had a bad injury with his shoulder and could not work so that was a down. My new mum could not have any children and was looking to adopt and I guess some kids would call me lucky I was adopted by her. I guess that was OK but sometimes I wish she didn't. We stayed in my home country for a while and then it was time to go back to London. ☹ Obviously I would not remember everything but this is what I was told.

Sometimes I would wish I could have stayed with my family even if it did mean me dying. Now I speak English and can't speak my own original home language. ☹ I am learning but I am still not very good. My new mum has said I can visit my original mum when I am 13 or 14. I am 12 at the moment and the one thing I think which is really going to annoy me is the fact I will not be able to say hi and I've missed you, etc. without my real mum not understanding.

I guess I have been quite lucky but even though I was adopted and have got everything I have needed I am still not happy and wish I never got adopted. Some might think I'm crazy but they would understand if they knew or felt how I felt. The one thing, if I could wish for anything, would be if I couldn't live with my parents I would wish my older brother would live with me in the UK so that I would always have a bit of my real family with me!

It's so hard to tell your friends I'm adopted but everyone in my school has been so nice to me about it and I've got some really nice friends.

From a blob to an athlete

Anthony (age 11)

Chapter One: From birth to three years old.

I was born in 1993 in a hospital in the East of England. I was very ill when I was born and I was in the special care baby unit in an incubator. I weighed 2,400 grams.

My mum was taking drugs when she was pregnant with me and so I was very ill and the doctors and nurses had to take the drugs out of my tummy. I stayed in hospital for three weeks.

Until I was three I lived some of the time with different foster parents and some of the time with my birth mum and birth dad. Sometimes I lived with foster parents from Monday to Friday and then went to my parents at the weekend. But I did not like swopping homes so much.

My birth mum did not look after me brilliantly. She took me to nursery and then forgot to collect me and my social worker had to come and pick me up. I was not very happy because sometimes there was no food to eat and I did not have clean clothes. My birth sister who was eight had to look after me and James because sometimes my birth mum went out and left us on our own.

One day I was in the baby walker and I fell over and banged my head. It bled for a long time and I still have a scar. It is about three inches long on the top of my head and it is so big that my hair cannot grow on it. When I was cold or bored I used to sit and rock backwards and forwards. My sister used to get cross with me for rocking.

My birth dad used to come round to visit us and take us out to the park on Saturdays. Sometimes he gave us money for sweets.

My social worker told my new parents that when I lived with my birth mum I was like a blob with legs, because all I used to do was sit on her knee whilst she drunk cans of beer. I did not walk very well. I could not go upstairs because my legs were not very strong. I was unhappy.

My social worker decided that I had to go to live in a different family and that I could not live with my birth parents any more, so in 1996, when I was almost three years old, I went into foster care full-time. My social worker told me she would find me a family I could live with forever.

Chapter Two: Living in a village, aged three and four

I went to live in a village. I lived in a family that thought I had learning difficulties. They kept me in nappies and they sent me to a special school. I had to go in a taxi every day on my own. I had to go nearly 20 miles with my own taxi driver.

My taxi driver bought me a Christmas present. My birth dad's mum, my nanny, lived in the same village. Sometimes we went to see her. The man who lived next to my foster parents' house was a fireman. He had a model of a fireman outside his house.

My birth sister lived in a different foster home. Sometimes my social worker took me to meet her and we went out places. I was still not very good at walking and I used to dribble a lot when I talked. In May 1998 I moved back to the city and went to live with a very nice lady called Dawn.

Chapter Three: A nice lady called Dawn, aged four and five

I went to live in the city with a lady called Dawn. She had a nice garden with lots of toys in it like swings, a trampoline and cars. I had my own bedroom. There was a playing field in front of Dawn's house and we used to play football there or we went on our bikes. Dawn did not think I should go to a special school so I went to school but I did reception year again. Dawn took us on lots of outings to the seaside and to an animal farm.

One day we went out with lots of other children for the day to a theme park. We went on a big truck and every child was taken on their own truck with a trucker. The people who drove the trucks paid for the day out. There were about 60 trucks going down the road in a convoy. It was good fun.

Dawn took us to help the St John's Ambulance people at a regional show. She had grandchildren. They were the same age as me and James. They used to come round a lot and play with us. Dawn took me to a church. She was kind and bought us sweets and chewing gum after we went to the dentist. She was sometimes strict but not very often. She was good fun to live with. I was happy living with Dawn but I still could not walk very well or run fast.

Chapter Four: Moving to London, aged six and seven

My social worker who was called Louise told me that I was going to live with a family in London. She told me my new mum and dad's names and said I was going to get two more brothers, Jack who was 14 and Stephen who was 13.

London was very big and noisy. My mum took us to places like Big Ben and *HMS Belfast*. My dad took us to the park a lot and began to teach me to play football.

We went on holiday to Scotland. We went on a long walk but I hated walking and moaned all the time that I was tired.

I started at school. My first teacher I had for two years in Year 1 and Year 2. When I started school I used to stand in the playground and cry because I did not have any friends.

When I had lived with my adoptive parents for about three months they took me to get my eyes tested. That was when they discovered I could not see very well. I got glasses and I could see a bit better.

I got a helper in class called Angie and got some friends. It took the school a long time to learn that I have to have my work in large print. They did not realise that my glasses did not make my eyes perfect and that I still could not see very well.

At playtimes I played with my friend. We liked playing "it" with some girls. When I was in Year 2 I was in the nativity play called *Jingle Bell Rock*. I played the inn keeper. I started to learn to swim. I joined Beavers and went on some outings with them. I went to a drama club called Time and Talents. I did not play football very well because I could not see the ball. We went on a camping holiday to France and I liked to go and get the croissants for breakfast every morning. I got used to living in London and began to speak with a London accent.

Chapter Five: Getting fitter, aged eight and nine

We went to New Zealand on holiday. I liked going on walks up the mountains. We went to see some seals and penguins. One of the best things was white water rafting and driving a jet boat.

At school I began to get better at my work and I learned to read books in large print. I went to drama club and choir. After school I went to swimming club and

I went to a football club but I was not very good. Sometimes we went ice-skating at an ice-rink. I started to go to Cubs and went camping.

My brother Jack left home and went to live in his own flat. We got an extension at the top of the house and because we had more bedrooms I got my own bedroom at last.

In Year 4, I joined the football coaching after school on Wednesdays. But lots of the other kids bullied me because I could not see the ball. My mum heard about football for visually impaired kids. I went to the training session at Arsenal and I began to get better at football. I went to my first sports camp and I tried Goal Ball and VI cricket for the first time. I met a friend who is totally blind and we got on well together.

We had a trampoline in the garden and I spent a lot of time jumping on it. My legs got a lot stronger. My other brother Stephen went to live in Kent.

My birth sister who is in foster care started to come and visit us every school holiday. I liked seeing her and we used to go to different places in London with her like the Monument and on a boat on the River Thames. In the summer holidays we went to France and I did a Nike football course at the campsite and it was good fun.

Chapter Six: Becoming an athlete, aged ten to eleven

When I was ten I woke up in our campervan in Italy and discovered that my mum and dad had decorated the gazebo with balloons and ribbons. We went to four different countries on tour in the campervan: France then Switzerland, then Italy and then Germany. It broke down going up a hill in Italy and we had to walk along the motorway to get help.

My teacher in Year 5 was kind and she taught me that it's OK to be adopted because she was adopted when she was a baby.

I got better at football and went to Aston Villa to play in the National 5 a side finals. I played for the Arsenal under 12s and we won the cup.

I went to Lords to play cricket and I met Andy Dolby Welsh who is in the England Blind Cricket team. I started to go to athletics with my brother James and I liked running middle distance. I came third in the district Cubs crosscountry run. When my dad did the Windsor half-marathon I did the 4km fun run and I finished it in 19.20.

I went to Nuneaton and did the British Blind Sports championships. I got three golds.

Now I am in Year 6. My teacher is in charge of PE. I am the sports monitor and sometimes I referee the Year 3 and 4 football matches at lunch time.

The Arsenal under 12s won at Aston Villa again. I played football for my school in a competition at another school. I like ICT and games.

When I leave school I would like to be a sports development officer. My favourite sport is football, then athletics, then cricket and I like going ice-skating if there is a lot of space on the ice. I do sport a lot after school. I go to an athletics club on Tuesdays and Thursdays. I do after-school football on Wednesdays and swimming club on Tuesdays. On Fridays I go to Scouts and on Saturdays and Sundays I do visually impaired football or athletics. So I had to buy a diary so I could fit everything in. When I am not playing sport I go to watch my football club play. So I am very busy because I have to do sport and homework and piano practice.

The future

I want to be a sportsman and help other children do sport. Sport has got me fit and strong and made me feel normal. I am one of the best people in my class at sport now. When I did the Bleep test I got to level 8/9 and I was very fit. I feel good when I run the same as other children. I could run forever because I feel really comfortable running.

Naila's family

Naila (age 7)

I have two mums. One mum is very arty and the other one is very good at writing and already has books published. Both mums care a lot about me and my two adopted sisters.

I lived with my foster family when I was a baby. My mums take me to see my foster family and we all get on very well together and I like playing with Zara who is five years old.

Me and my middle sister like playing together. We both like playing imaginary games like the fairy Lava game. We like going camping and sometimes we go to France. Every Easter we go to the Island of Islay and stay in a house with no electricity. The beach is right next to the cottage. We go on lots of walks and we like playing on the beach with our cheetah and lion toys.

Some people think that you shouldn't have two mums but they are so wrong.

Podcast with Jordan

Jordan (age 16)

Kim Graham (Senior Adoption Practitioner, CCS Adoption, a small independent adoption agency based in Bristol): I am talking to a young man today who is nearly 17 who is an adopted person. He has kindly agreed to talk about his experiences. He wasn't able to stay with the family he was born into and was placed in foster care when he was four years old and then he went to live with his adoptive parents when he was seven.

Kim: How did you feel when you first found out that you were going to move from your foster family to your adoptive family?

Jordan: To be frank, it was very difficult and just seeing that, feeling the changes, you're settled in a family, you're settled and you're just like, 'Oh no, not again. I'm moving.' You just think to yourself, 'out of control', just everything's gone, all over the place, just no support, you're moving again. Why can't I just stop stay here? I'm settled, I have friends.

Kim: And what was it like meeting your adoptive parents for the first time?

Jordan: It was very different just to meet yet another family. It was just like after a line of people you think, 'Are these going to be the people I stay with for the next however long or is this just going to be another foster family?'

Kim: And how long do you think it took for you to be a little bit settled in your new family?

Jordan: I think it's got to be three years just to feel slightly settled and more secure in the home but it's ongoing. You don't feel completely settled. You still have anxiety every now and again of just, is this going to end or is this it? Am I staying here?

Kim: Once you settled in, how have things gone and have there been any challenges along the way?

Jordan: Things have started off a bit rough when I was sort of less mature and more all over the place, bouncy sort of teenager type person when arguments threw up. That's just normal family isn't it? You just bounce about, have a laugh and the next minute you are arguing over something stupid. But I mean the main challenge is crossing the borderline between maturity and that bouncy teenager. Just becoming more mature and saying, 'Look, that's it. Let's sort of chill out now and give something back to the support that I have from my parents.'

Kim: How was it when you actually had to start a new life, particularly starting a new school at seven years old? Can you remember much about that experience?

Jordan: I remember a bit. At seven you just, you just don't really remember a lot, you just pick out the bigger bits. And moving to a new school you're leaving behind all the friends you've got to know in six months. You change teachers that you've known for a while, new friends, a whole new life, a new family. Moving into that is very difficult and strenuating really. Your emotions are all over the place, you're very worried about what's going to happen, if you're going to be OK in the year you're in, if you're going to get bullied, things like that.

Kim: And how did your adoptive parents help you to settle in?

Jordan: They were very helpful. They were always there to support me, just there, always. If I had a problem I'd tell them and they'd try and sort it out for me. The first couple of days, week or so it's always tricky because it's a new school, new people. It's the same even if you are not adopted, it's always difficult. Meeting new friends was fun, meeting new people, a different life, different parts of the world. After a while you start to enjoy it, you stop being worried. Yeah, if you're going to get bullied and it happens, you just try to sort it out. It's the way things go.

Kim: What contact have you had with CCS over the years?

Jordan: CCS have been really friendly. I've had a really nice social worker who I just talk to if you have problems. If things are going wrong, difficult, don't be afraid to speak to them, they're always going to be there. I mean they have events during the year where you can go and talk with other people who've been through similar things. And just to get different experiences or similar experiences to your own, and talk about them openly. It's fun. You get to sort of just relax talking about what you've been through. You understand a bit more what other people have gone through. Also, the young people have a group where they gather and talk about everything, sort of trade comments on events that have happened and explore different ways of solving different problems in an open group with people that are a similar age. That's always been handy. If you've got something that's been on your mind, you just open up about it and they'll be there just to sort it out, give you ways of removing the fear or pain or anxiety that you have.

Kim: How do you feel adoption has helped you?

Jordan: In a way it's shown me a new path, it's given me a new light, it's given me hope that I'll be happy instead of feeling down 24/7 because I can't find anywhere that I want to stay. Going through adoption is difficult but once you're through it it's good; you feel safe, secure, you feel in a family which is always going to be there; you can ask for what you like because they're your parents, they're there, that's it, that's your family. You don't have to almost forget your past life but you'll never be able to truly forget it. All that you've been through will always be in your memory whatever age you are. It will just be there, a memory, just a memory.

Kim: Do you still think about your past and the family that you were born into?

Jordan: I have always wondered what has happened to them. Are they still as one? Are there offspring? Do they have more? Are they regretting moving on without me or putting me into foster [care]? It's always going to be a wonder and I hope sometime that I'll find out but if I don't, then oh well. It will just be an interesting thing to know. I'm always allowed to be open with my parents about it and talk to them because my mum was similar; she was adopted. So, that's always been great, to talk to somebody else close who's been adopted. That way you can exchange thoughts, ideas and just see how it went for them and just talk about it because talking's always good. If you've got something on your mind don't keep it there. Express it in words or an image or something. Get it out.

Kim: And if you wanted to find out more information later on and maybe trace the family you were born into, would you want to have the support of your parents? You'd hope to have the support of your parents?

Jordan: I think definitely I'd love to have the support of parents, friends, colleagues. I mean at CCS they have people, staff in there which I've known for a while, they'll always be friendly. If I was to trace then I'd hope that I'd have the support of everyone there, just hoping it all goes well. If it doesn't then I'd still look for support in others to guide me through it because I'd be a bit nervous as to what happens.

Kim: Well, thank you very much for talking to me today.

Jordan: And to you.

Acknowledgement: You can listen to Jordan's podcast on http://www.ccsadoption.org/Podcasts.htm

The beginning of me

Julia (at age 14)

I was born into the world small, weak and powerless

Given a name, clothed, hugged now motherless

No one to call my own

No place to call a home

I slept for a while, curled up in a ball

All fragile and alone. Would anyone love me at all?

My question was answered because the next day

A lovely couple arrived who took me to play

They cuddled me and fed me, they promised me a new start

They said I had a special place deep in their heart

They have looked after me since then, almost 14 years

Through the laughter, the anger and the uncontrollable tears

They are the best people in the world and I will love them forever

Mum, Dad and Jack, I love you and will leave you never

My story so far

Eoin Andrei (age 8)

Hi, my name is Eoin and I live in Ireland and I was adopted from Romania. I live in a small village. So what adopted means to me. I am so lucky to have a family. I am in Ireland for eight years now and I have a brother called Oisin. He is adopted too and he is from Russia. Sometimes I am sad because I miss my mam and dad in Romania.

My name is Josh

Josh (age 6)

My name is Josh. I am six years old. I live with my mammy and my daddy and my brother Mark. My parents adopted me when I was seven months old. I was born in Dublin and now I live in County Clare. My birth mother is Irish and my birth father is African. My foster mother Anita, who minded me very well when I was a tiny baby, died last month. My brother is adopted too. I have lots of friends and I go to school in Clonmoney. I am in senior infants.

Sobia's life story

Sobia (age 11)

My name is Sobia, I am Asian and I am adopted. I am 11 years old and I will soon be 12. I am deaf and I wear two hearing aids. I also have an auditory processing disorder (that means a memory problem). I have lived with my parents for ten years. I have two mums called Nita and Clare. They are lesbians. I also live with my grandparents and my two sisters who are also adopted. I have had some hard times, some sad times and some happy times.

I was adopted when I was 16 months old. Before I lived with my two mums, I lived first with my birth mum and then with my foster family. I lived with my birth mum for three weeks. She had some problems and couldn't look after me. Later I found out I had a younger birth brother and I went to see him before he was adopted. Now I write letters to my birth parents and my birth brother every year and they write to me. I like to get letters from them because I miss them. I also write to my foster family and sometimes I visit them. I enjoy visiting them.

My mums have been very kind to me because they have taken me to Pakistan and India which I have enjoyed a lot. First I went to India with both my sisters and then I went to Pakistan. It was very hot.

I like having two mums because it's fun and they understand about my problems and adoption. My friends have always known that my parents are lesbians and they think it is fine. They have never bullied me or done anything horrible to me.

My story

Jane (age 17)

My name is Jane. I have Foetal Alcohol Syndrome. I have it because my mother was an alcoholic. My speech, hearing, auditory processing, my heart and stomach were affected. I spent a month in intensive care with projectile vomiting, bowel infection and a heart murmur. I had an operation to stop the vomiting and get rid of the bowel infection. The heart murmur went away when I was five. I was a very small baby due to my mother's drinking; I am still quite short for my age. My jaw and teeth were also affected; my teeth were very twisted.

I am healthy now but the long-lasting effect has been on my brain. My auditory processing is very slow and I also have trouble with my memory. This means that I can only follow one instruction at a time and I often quickly forget what I'm supposed to be doing. I only hear one in three words so I take a long time to respond. This means friendships are difficult because I have trouble following a group conversation.

This means I also have trouble at school and with learning. Trying to follow a teacher's conversation is difficult. I often get the wrong idea of what I'm learning and my homework. I need help with note-taking because I'm not fast enough to write it all down before the teacher goes on to the next thing. I need one-to-one conversation with the teacher so I can understand what I'm doing.

After a psychologist who understands Foetal Alcohol Syndrome tested me, he wrote a report for the teachers and they were able to help me much better. I also had learning support workers in some of my lessons.

When I was younger I had speech therapy and later I had special listening from a private SpLD [Specific Learning Difficulty] teacher. At primary school I was told off a lot for doing things I shouldn't because I hadn't heard what the teacher said. In the morning before school I used to stand by myself because I didn't know how to socialise and approach people and the other kids found me difficult to talk to.

Secondary school was the same because I had the same problems so I was often on my own so people started to bully me and call me names because they thought I was weird because I was usually on my own. If people asked me to sit with them at lunch I would stay by myself. Because I felt very unsafe and tense around new people and I felt safer by myself, though it made me very lonely. Though I wanted to be with them I never felt like I fitted in because I was quiet because I wasn't good at socialising with new people. Sometimes people would tease me because I took a long time to respond or I hadn't heard what the person had said so they thought I was not clever.

Now I'm at college doing animal care and I get the right sort of help straight away so work is easier. I also have made some friends.

Fostering and adoption

Sophie (age 12)

I woke up in a room,
That I had never seen.
When I opened up my eyes,
There was someone looking down at me.

We spent years together,
And got closer than ever.
And whatever happens,
We'll stay in touch for ever.

Then I got adopted,
And began from the start.
I now have a new family
That has a very big heart.

My dad is an accountant,
My mum works at school.
She once was my headteacher.
Isn't that just so cool!

So I've known her for a long time,
But I've only just met him.
I have two new uncles.
One is called Graham and one is called Tim.

I am very happy,
In this lovely new home.
We have our ups and downs,
But we all try hard not to moan.

Now this poem's ending,
And I am saying goodbye.
I will love my new family
Until the day I die.

My family

Michael (at age 10)

Hi

I am Mike. I live with my mum, my dad

And my sister.

I live in a big house.

Me and my sister Katie always argue but eventually we hug

and make up.

Me and my mum sometimes quarrel, but same as me and my

sister we will make up.

My dad is always playing tricks on me and causing pandemonium,

Imagine what we are like.

Anyway we get along most of the time.

My identity

Luis (age 11)

Who am I?
Where do I live?

I live beyond the darkened waters and
beyond the blue sky, before you see
I am no England boy. I am further
than that, for my country where I
was born. My birth mother was forlorn
she was unhappy in her country of
Guatemala, because a new baby will
be born with the name of Luis
Arturo Gatica, so when that baby was
seven months old, he was sent to
some new prawns, so he thought anyway,
for these people were like white
sausages; of many a person, these
were the oddest and for this reason
in the future here I am a boy of
eleven with those pink prawns which I
don't think are prawns anymore so
a fine new life has sprung up so
HIP! HIP! HURRAH!!! HIP! HIP! HOORAY!!!

Happy being adopted

Christina Cole-Wilson (age 18)

Dictated by Christina to her adoptive mother

I am happy being adopted by my mum. I have been living with my mum and my brother for 16 years. I was two when I came to live with them and we had a party; it was my aunt's birthday on the day I came.

It was nice to come in the world – my mum met me at the foster home. I remember the photo of my mum cuddling me.

We went to court for the adoption. The judge was very nice. He gave me a big tin to choose some sweets and I said I wanted to take one for my brother but he says, 'These are specially for you, your brother can have one later'.

It's nice being adopted. I'm happy and I enjoy being with my family and having fun. I like having nice food like joloff rice and junk food – fish and chips, liver and bacon, foo foo, palava sauce and groundnut stew. I love my mum's cooking and my nan's cooking and all my aunts and uncles.

I got christened and confirmed and I've got lots of grandparents. I had lots of presents when I came.

This year it was my 18th birthday and we went out for a meal and cocktails in a limousine.

I have been to lots of places: Majorca, Germany, Sierra Leone, Barbados, Colorado, Disney Orlando, Ibiza and lots of other places. This year we are going maybe to New York. My mum is taking me and my brother because I was 18 in August and my brother was 21 in August.

My brother is very nice and he's caring and loving. He is good at music and cooking, he is very creative.

I have a niece, Saraya, who is one year and nine months old.

When I first came I felt I didn't know where I was but afterwards it was good, living in a different house with my new family. Now they are not my new family; they are my old family.

I feel good about myself. I am happy, lively, bubbly, good sometimes and sometimes I am mischievous when I want to get my own way. Sometimes I get my own way and sometimes I don't.

I am a Christian and I celebrate Christmas and Easter. I like going to church with either my mother or godmother. I have recently been away with the church for a long weekend.

It is nice being adopted by someone who looks like me.

It is nice living with a single parent because sometimes you get to go out and have fun.

My mum is a lesbian. It's different and strange but it's also lovely to have another person around sometimes.

I would like to visit the countries where my birth family came from.

I'm OK about being adopted.

I am an adult now so I am going to start searching for my birth family.

My hopes for the future are to move home and go into some sort of sheltered accommodation and be independent. I would like to make my own CDs and would like a job but I'm not sure what I want to do yet. I like working with children but I've also thought about being a chef or a counsellor, dancer or singer.

Different

Nathan Glazier (age 12)

'Oi!' I could tell it was one of the ring leaders, Shane, by the sound of his voice, so aggressive! I didn't turn around. I didn't even want to look at him.

'Oi, you, the kid who was such a piece of junk that his real mum didn't want him ... actually she probably didn't love him!' he jeered. 'I mean, what a slapper getting pregnant at 14!' he said, then he smacked me in the back.

That was it, I'd had enough of this, it had been happening for too long now. I turned around and punched him full blow in the mouth. That is not what I'd normally do but this time he'd gone too far! It had been happening for months, since the day I started at my senior school everyone had something against me, even kids I didn't know! Kids had jeered about me being adopted most times but no one had gone this far. But, I thought, the one person I could rely on was my head of year, as the teachers didn't do anything to help me even if it happened in the class! My head of year was supposed to punish people appropriately for bullying, but she couldn't even do that. Well, yeah, the occasional exclusion but it never worked – they still carried on bullying me! I don't hit back usually because I want to stay out of trouble. Shane hit me on the chest, I pushed him, then he grabbed my head and hit it up against the wall a few times. While he was doing so the teacher walked in!

Lucy and Jane – two of a kind

Karen Ulyana Roche (at age 7)

Once upon a time there was a girl called Jane. She was four years old and she was adopted. One day Jane asked her mam why she was adopted. Her mam said, because your mammy was not able to look after you. But her mam said there are loads of different ways why other children are adopted. Jane was looking forward to telling her teacher in playschool what she learned. Her mam said that she was going to a Russian culture because she was adopted from Russia. Jane asked when she was going. Next Saturday, said her mam. Jane was excited.

When Saturday came Jane got up very early and woke her mam up. Jane was jumping on her bed saying I'm going to a Russian culture. Her mam said she was going to wear her best clothes which were her black shoes and her pink dress. When they got to the Russian culture, the person's name was Inna. She was from Russia. Inna said they were going to make Russian dolls; Inna said if you want you can have a spare set. Jane said yes, she would like a spare set to bring with her.

That evening when Jane went home she sat down in front of the fire. Her mam said to Jane that night they were going to the house of a lady called Maureen tomorrow to celebrate Russian Easter. Jane was excited. When she woke up that morning she went into her mammy's room. When she went into her mam's room she said they were going to Maureen's house to celebrate Russian Easter. There was a special Russian cake there. It had raisins, fruit and icing on the top. It was a tall cake. Maureen cut the top of the cake and cut it into slices. Everyone got a slice so Maureen said she needed to re-ice the cake for another time. That evening when Jane went home she got into her nightdress and went to bed. And when she fell asleep she had lovely dreams. When she woke up that morning she told her mam about her best dream. She said in her dream she jumped over the moon.

Her mam had some good news. She said a new couple had moved next door. Jane went to say hello to the new people. She was talking to the people and they were saying that they had a child named Lucy adopted from China and she was four like Jane. After one week Jane and Lucy were best friends. One evening Lucy and Jane were making up a dance where Lucy twirls twice, then Jane jumps three times very high. The next day her mam had to book her into school. She saw Lucy's mammy there too. When she went home she told Jane that Lucy was going to be in the same class and school. Jane was very happy.

That evening Jane told Lucy about the Russian culture. Jane had an idea. She could give Lucy her spare set of Russian dolls. Lucy said thank you to Jane. When Lucy went home she showed her mam what Jane had given her. Jane's mam and Lucy's mam said that they were starting school next week. When Monday came Jane had butterflies in her tummy. When she got into her school she had to line up. Lucy was in front of her in the line. When the children got into the classroom the teacher introduced herself. Her name was Ruth Kelly but everyone called her Ms Kelly.

When Lucy showed Ms Kelly her dolls that Jane gave her she said that the whole class could make the dolls. Since Jane and Lucy were adopted, Ms Kelly decided to teach the class a little about adoption: how different families are formed and why children are adopted. On Friday they did art. For their art they did the Russian dolls. Lucy did hers in the Russian colours which were white, blue, red and white. On Saturday Lucy and Jane were talking about why they were adopted. Jane said because her mammy was not able to look after her and Lucy said she was adopted because the law in China would not let her mammy keep her but she said her mammy did love her and did want to keep her. That evening Lucy and Jane said they would ask their mammy and daddy for some more information about adoption.

That evening Lucy and Jane were talking about what they had learned in school. Lucy said Ms Kelly was a good teacher and a nice teacher. Jane agreed with Lucy. That night Lucy had a dream about 'she was in China' seeing her birth parents. When she told Jane about her dream, Jane said she was going to have a dream like that that night.

The next day in school a boy came over to both of them and said, 'You two are adopted because your mammies did not like you'. Jane said that was not true. When she went home she told her mam about that boy saying that horrible thing to Lucy and Jane.

One day in school they were talking about what they were going to be when they grow up. Ms Kelly asked Jane what she was going to be. Jane said she was going to be a social worker. Ms Kelly said she is a social worker sometimes too. When Jane went home she told her mammy that her teacher is a social worker sometimes. The next day Ms Kelly gave all the children in the class a note.

When Lucy and Jane walked home Lucy said to Jane, 'Do you know anything about Russian Christmas?' Jane said yes, she did know something about Russian Christmas. Jane said Santa was called Old Man Frost and he travelled with a snow maiden and four horses. Jane asked Lucy if she knew anything about Christmas in China. When Lucy went home that evening she asked her mam how they celebrate Christmas in China. Her mam told her. The next day Lucy said to Jane, 'This is how they celebrate Christmas in China. Christmas in China is celebrated by lighting their houses with beautiful paper lanterns and decorating their Christmas trees, which they call trees of light, with paperchains, paper flowers and paper lanterns. Chinese children hang muslin stockings and await a visit from Santa Claus, who they call *Dun Che Lao Ren* which means Christmas Old Man.' Jane asked how you pronounce Santa Claus in Chinese – Lucy said, 'Just say it after me – *dwyn-chuh-lau-oh-run*.' Jane was very happy that Lucy told her how they celebrate Christmas in China.

The next day in school Jane told the teacher how Jane and Lucy discussed Russian Christmas and Christmas in China. The teacher said she would teach the class how they celebrate Christmas in China on Monday and Christmas in Russia on Tuesday. The children were all very happy. So was Ms Kelly.

Next week it was Lucy's birthday. She invited Jane. When Lucy gave Jane the invitation Jane showed her mam. Her mam said she could go. When Lucy's birthday came Lucy said to Jane she is thinking about her tummy mummy. One day when Lucy and Jane were walking home Jane asked Lucy when is Mother's Day. Lucy said in two weeks. When Mother's Day came they were both thinking about their tummy mummy. Jane told Lucy what she does on special occasions. She said she lights a candle in the church for her tummy mummy. On the last day of school Jane and Lucy were walking home from school when Lucy said, 'I like being adopted'. Jane said, 'You know what, Lucy? So do I.'

THE END

My family

Solome (age 8)

My family

25 June 2008

Hi! I am Solome. I am 8 years old. I'm
going to be 9 on the 28 of July. I have
two brothers. One is older then me
and one is yonger then me. I am
adopted. I have a mum and
dad from Ireland. My dad is
half bold. I finish school on
the 25 of june. I was born in 1999.
I am good at art. I love my
family!

Adaptation

Francis Davies (age 17)

So here is one of the few times I have tried to put down what I think and feel about all this. It's hard, not just because it sucks, but because I'm not crystal clear how I feel about it all. I'll try to do this without the whole 'woe is me, I grew up fucked' theme. No one really wants to listen to me whine on about my sob story; including me.

The way I see it now is this. Every so often you'll get the question, 'If you could go back in time and change something, what would you change?' It might be on a Myspace quiz, or on some random questionnaire, or just something someone randomly asks for the hell of it. Nevertheless, everyone runs into this question at some point in their lives. To hell with it. Despite everything that has happened, despite all the anger and pain that my childhood caused me, I wouldn't change it.

You'd think that after getting dragged away from my mother at five, put into foster care until I was eight going on nine and still dealing with it at 17, I would jump at the chance to change all that. Personally I'd change nothing. What happened to me and the effects of that have made me who I am. It forged the way I look at life, how I deal with things. It has made who and what I am. 'What doesn't kill you only makes you stronger' holds a lot of meaning for me. I'm not dead yet and after that, I'd say I was pretty damn strong now.

Becoming a teenager is pretty fun, right? You get to drink, do drugs, party and stay up late pretty much at least once a week. In a lot of cases people from about 13 to 16 are busy drinking cause so are their mates and they have to fit in and be cool, right? Yeah. Damn glad I had the experience I had to give me the first-hand knowledge not to take up drinking everything under the sun to prove how much of a man I am, or do drugs to prove that I'm cool enough to fit in. Cause hey, when my liver fails and I'm in hospital at 16 for excessive drinking, being cool doesn't exactly cut it. No matter how up to date your tombstone is. Same thing with overdosing or lung cancer. And while I am at it, my mum really didn't look very 'cool' slumped in a heap on her bed with a few cans scattered around her, or staggering down the hall leaning on the wall for support. I am proud to have gone through early teenage years without feeling the need to be comatose throughout it.

Aside from resisting peer pressure and all that stuff, I'd say I'm just generally stronger for it. I have issues, but then after that childhood, who doesn't? I don't need pity, I don't ask for pity, I don't require constant attention and I'm tired of all these kids who have decided that being depressed is cool, have decided that because mummy grounded them they can go and see a psychiatrist, mope around with their mates and claim that their lives suck. I have a feeling that if these kids knew what depression is really like, they'd stop glamourising it. And since when did manic depressives go around proclaiming their mental conditions to the world in large groups?

I deal with my anger and the depression I had up until about 14 or 15 isn't bad anymore. I still get small occasional bouts but generally, as I work my way through my past, it's diminished. It still hurts, but I think most of my depression was because I didn't completely understand it or know quite how to deal with it. Now it's nearly all rage, that's been there since this started – it's just controlled a lot better. Up until a few years ago I was a wreck. I'd flip out and lash out at anything that caused me pain, inanimate object included. Who am I kidding? I still do that. But it takes more for that reaction than it used to. That's good, both for my knuckles, my feet and everything else. Aside from that, I am finding ways to calm myself down if I start getting wound up.

Now I'm nearing my 18th birthday and legally my genetic mother is allowed to come find me. It's probably quite mean to her, but I hope she doesn't. Or at least not yet. If she was to show up on my doorstep anytime over the next few years, it's probably going to destroy a whole lot of my security. I couldn't deal with seeing her now, it would bring everything just flooding right back again, whether she's sober or not. I couldn't deal with that. I don't think I ever could really. But not now.

At the end of this I'm still no clearer than I was before. It's getting easier as I grow up, but I suppose things do. Overall when it comes down to it I've adapted to what's been thrown my way. I've dragged myself along and come out of the other end mostly intact. That's how humans evolved and got their way in the world. Guess I feel like a miniature version of that.

My family

Luke Howard (at age 6)

I came with my problems – they helped me solve them
I came with my memories – they listened to them
I have my differences – they liked them
I brought my love – they shared theirs with me

Everybody is different

Luke Howard (at age 6)

My mum and dad have lots of children. When I came to be adopted I was not ill then. When I got ill I thought they might be sad and wish they had got a boy with no bad bones. I never thought before being black was sad for them. I know I am good with just how I am. Everybody is different not just me, Daddy says so.

Acknowledgement: 'My family' and 'Everybody is different' by Luke Howard were first published in Harris P (ed.) (2006), *In Search of Belonging: Reflections by transracially adopted people*, London: BAAF

My adoption story

Jess Peterson (age 15)

Fire, I thought. The washing machine in the garden has set the house ablaze – my worst nightmare had come true. Heart pounding, I bravely stepped down the stairs and into the living room. From there I could see the garden clearly – and the washing machine was still lying on its side where me and dad had put it that afternoon when it had started to smoke. So what was the problem?

When I looked into the room I could see my dad lying on the sofa on his back and out of breath, as if he had just run the London marathon. It was only then that I saw my mum standing at the other side of the room, clutching the telephone and screaming for the ambulance. It was her screaming that had woken me up. When she saw me she was in hysterics. She didn't want me to see my dad like this. 'Quick! Run and get help now!'

At this I jumped to and, with only one slipper, ran to our neighbours' house two doors away, as they were the only people I knew would help. I knocked on the door and as I waited, I thought about what was happening. Being only seven, I didn't fully understand what was going to happen to Dad, but I had worked out the general gist of it. When my friend answered, she was puzzled as to why I was calling after bedtime. I asked for her parents and when they came to the door I can distinctly remember saying, 'I think my daddy's dying.'

They ran straight round to our house with me in tow. When I got home I crept upstairs to my sleeping three-year-old brother, who hadn't heard anything downstairs. I sat in his room until Mum came up to say that Dad was very ill and that she would be going to the hospital with him while we were to go to my friend's. Then she left. After another hour or so she came back up, but was followed by a paramedic who asked questions about Dad's health, like did he smoke and did he eat sweets. When she left Mum told us that Dad was dead. I was given the option to stay at home or go to my friend's anyway, and I decided to stay with my friend – the idea that someone had died in our house scared me.

As I sat on their sofa shared with three other people all fast asleep, it started to sink in that my dad was never going to crack funny jokes, or laugh, or look after me when I was hurt. But, being only seven, I never really was going to understand death the way I do now, especially that of your own father, and it was only then that I started to cry.

This is an extract of something I wrote a couple of years ago, when I wanted to write my life's memories for me to keep.

My name is Jess Peterson but I used to be known as Jessica Valen. I am now 15 years old and live with my mum, dad and brother in a village in Berkshire, England. My late father was pure English, however my mother was half-Caribbean. My hobbies include riding and playing the piano.

I can only remember the larger details of the night my dad died, so I can't really remember what my feelings were. Looking back, I think I probably wanted to pretend that it all wasn't happening, because I did want to go to school the very next day.

For me, this was the beginning of a downward spiral, because only 13 months later my mum died of breast cancer. I tried to get on with life as normal, with the smallest changes possible, and I found that really easy to manage. Again, I can't actually remember feeling any sort of emotion at all – it was as if my mind was closing down all the bad stuff. However, I did and still do miss my birth parents, and always will, because they didn't deserve to die, no one does.

I love my new life and my new parents, and I settled in really quickly. I don't think about what life would have been like if my parents were still alive – I find I don't have the time! I've also accepted that it's never going to happen, so there's no point in wishing it.

When my mum was hospitalised for the last time my brother and me were taken to live with various relatives, never lasting more than a few months. That was when they decided to have us adopted. I never hated moving or the idea of adoption, but the one place that made me think more about it was when we went to stay with a "friend" of my mum's who had three children of her own, all older than me. She was kind enough to let us live there, I'll give her that, but she picked on my brother so much, I felt I had to stop it. So it came as an enormous relief when we were fostered.

We stayed with a couple that had fostered children of our age before, so they knew how to treat us. But we were fine and loved living with them – they were the closest things to parents I'd had in a long time, and I felt totally relaxed.

They introduced me to Brownies. I started Year 4 with a few good friends and had my ninth birthday partying at a Scouts' club hall. But it wasn't long before we were told that they had found us a couple that wanted to adopt us.

I recently read in my adoption records that I had written a letter to the adoption agency asking for a new family 'as quickly as possible', though I can't recall ever doing that! But I think it spoke out for what I was feeling – I loved being fostered, but I really needed a new home and family. So I was all up for this family who lived on a farm!

I wasn't nervous when they first knocked on the door and I answered. My brother and I introduced ourselves, and vice versa. Then they took us out to the park. It was a great feeling to be totally relaxed around them, and I knew that they were just the sort of family I wanted. When we first went to visit their house, the first thing I did was race upstairs and try to find my room, which had been decorated especially. We took it slowly at first, only staying the afternoon and then the day and then finally the whole night. I loved it.

About two days before we were meant to move there permanently we were running late, so they offered us the chance to stay the night again. But, for the first time, I felt almost homesick. I wanted to be at home where I was familiar and I could see that this upset my new parents. But they understood and took me home. I don't know why I wanted to go home. I suppose that I wanted as much time with my foster parents as possible because I felt I owed it to them to say a proper goodbye and not to leave them earlier than I had to. But I don't think they would have minded though! Having said that, I had no more problems and moved away very calmly and easily, knowing that this was the beginning of a new life, a life that I had been waiting for for a few long, sad months.

I have one picture in my room that suggests I wasn't always here – a picture of my birth mum and dad smiling together, and it sits above my bed. It is a very comforting thing to have, because it's as if they are watching me grow up and have fun, like any normal teenager would, and I will never forget them and what they meant to me once upon a time.

On making Anna

Anna Maria Silvia (age 7)

Take 89 litres of Guatemalan blood
Add 100 grams of Mummy Silvia's bones
Mix in 900 little pieces of Daddy Hector's flesh
Drop in my big sister Jackie's kindness
Heat gently under a smoking volcano

Flip the fragile mixture into an aeroplane
Pour in Mummy Judy's beautiful smile
And stir for 8 months
Then cut up slices of cuddles from Grandpa and Grandma
Whip in my Uncle Chris's jokes and my Auntie Pauline's make-up
And bake in a wonderful home in England
Forever

© Anna Maria Silvia 2008

Excerpts

Kevin Toni Mitchell (at age 18)

Family is about belonging to something greater than yourself.

I was given away by the only person I ever truly belonged to.

*   *   *

At a young age I was told about how I came to be in the family.

I don't know that it helped me understand though. I understood the words I was told but I couldn't fathom what they meant. The words seemed so irreconcilably at odds with what my parents were trying to communicate.

I read somewhere that communication is only seven per cent verbal but no amount of tone or body language could communicate what they were trying to tell me in ways that a five-year-old could understand.

'Your mummy loved you very much but she couldn't look after you, so she gave you away.'

From the way that I was told this it was clear that it was important. Children are not supposed to question serious and important things, so I didn't, at least not openly anyway. I went through the motions; I solemnly nodded to show I understood. But the questions I asked and the arguments they provoked were only ever with myself.

*   *   *

The thing that is most memorable of childhood years was the doubtless expectation that I had.

I was supremely confident that it was all a big misunderstanding and that sooner rather than later my mum would arrive, make her apologies, hug me, tell me she loved me and whisk me off to where I was supposed to be.

Every weekend we'd go on a family trip somewhere (they were really good like that) whether it was a museum, country park or a roman fort, weekends were for outings. They were always an inventive mix of fun and education.

They'd never tell me where we were going; instead they would say we were going to 'w and s for w and s' (wait and see – one of grandma's favourite things to say).

That's all they had to do, say those magic words, hint at something special and stand back to watch me jump up and down with excitement.

I would jolt forward against my seatbelt to try and make the car go faster. Anything to get there quicker.

Picture the scene: me, a little boy of five years old, waiting for his mum to return and collect him, certain it all happened by mistake, being told that, 'We're going somewhere special this weekend.'

'Where? Tell me where! What are we doing?'

'You'll have to w and s,' was the inevitable reply.

Certain that this would be the day I would get all excited and go over in my head what she looked like so that I'd recognise her.

I'd try and remember all the manners I'd been taught so she would see that I was nice and polite and then maybe she would be proud.

There are 52 weekends in every year and in my stupidity I looked forward to every one of them.

I don't know whether I can accurately describe what it felt like each time I realised she wasn't coming.

The boundless enthusiasm of my Saturday mornings was in stark contrast to the crushing disappointment of my Saturday afternoons.

* * *

I remember introductions. I'd be playing on the monkey-bars in a park, meet some like-minded child and after all the usual posturing and machismo – 'I can swing across faster than you can' – provided a suitably impressive reply was offered up, you'd grant temporary best buddy status.

For the next 20 to 30 minutes, you'd be having the time of your life running about like a lunatic with your new partner in crime. Being a soldier, a cowboy, an astronaut, being anything but being "normal" and feeling "normal".

Then the parents would arrive and the illusion was over.

The parents would make small talk amongst themselves, as I looked at my feet and willed the earth to swallow me, 'This is our son Kevin'.

The other child's parents look slightly confused, but are too polite ask what they are clearly thinking. 'Nice to meet you,' they'd say.

Being too young to know what-not-to-ask, my former buddy asks the obvious, 'Why are you a different colour to them?'

'He's adopted,' is my father's cheerful reply, blissfully unaware that I died each time I heard that.

By this point I'm tugging at Mum's sleeve with no small amount of urgency, wanting to avoid further questions that will only intensify the shame and embarrassment of a stranger being told you were given away.

* * *

I am the offspring of parents I have never met, the product of a failed relationship. I am a dirty secret and a painful reminder of the mistake they both made.

The last remnant of a life hastily forgotten, an unfinished chapter in an unpleasant story, I am officially "illegitimate".

I know what it is to feel abandoned and alone, worthless and unwanted. I knew these feelings long before I had words for them. It felt bad at the time and little has changed.

Part white and part black, I am hopelessly both and yet neither.

The problem is that we do live in a world divided along racial lines and to deny the issue is to compound the problem. We should embrace the differences in culture and custom and see that variety enriches our lives but we don't.

As long as difference arouses suspicion more readily than stereotypes provoke challenges, I must accept that I can never belong.

Too white for blacks and too black for whites, what a thing it is to be brown!

I have no identity. I am a stranger in the mirror.

I don't know where I'm from, can only hope at where I'm headed, and all the while I'm acutely aware that it's only me that really cares and even I'm beginning not to. I have a chip on both shoulders and fists in both hands. I don't know how not to be angry.

* * *

Sitting here alone, trying to write a self-help book in the dim light of a flat I can't afford, I am not happy.

Independence is such a glass-half-full take on being alone. It's as though the word should come with an asterix followed by a disclaimer in small print: I am deeply disillusioned with it.

Alone is a strong and perhaps unusual word to describe an 18-year-old, the youngest of a large family.

On the increasingly infrequent occasions that we do meet as a family, hugs are customary, not comfortable. I never felt the closeness I have seen depicted in countless films. Perhaps such relationships are entirely the domain of film and fiction; if they are then I'm glad.

I can be alone in a room full of people, it's like being able to touch but not feel.

* * *

We have polite conversations from time to time, expressing mild interest in each other's affairs but these conversations are more out of a sense of obligation than out of a wish for involvement.

We exchange words and none of them contain any malice or ill feeling but that's just it: they don't contain any feeling at all. The words are empty and meaningless; they don't convey feelings or carry comfort.

Though it's an insult to their efforts over the years, I don't have parents in a conventional sense. The paternal bonds that exist for others are not to be found between me and my parents.

I sometimes wonder how long after my parents stopped trying to build bridges, did I stop trying to burn them. Too late is the only answer I arrive at.

had glasses and wore a brace on my teeth they never wanted to know me. I even stopped wearing my glasses but it didn't help.

In my final year at school I always knew what I wanted to do. I wanted to be a nurse. I never had problems with friends. My final year seemed to go well. I worked really hard for my exams and got good GCSEs. I got into college and made some nice friends. I started college in September. I went on the Advanced Health & Social Care course. The college told me it was the right course for nursing. I thought my life was finally going the way I planned.

Children's grief

Heather (Nan Ziyuan) Macrae (at age 8)

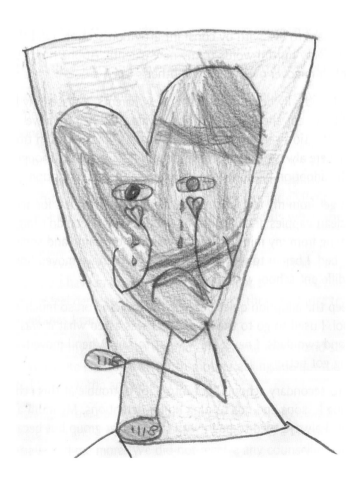

Being a mother

Terezia Dziubak (age 20)

It's difficult because I've never had much emotional warmth from sets of parents (biological and adoptive). What are you supposed to do? I found it hard to bond with my son when he was born, so his father Rodney had to take over.

Even though he had a severe drinking problem which is an illness, I knew at the time he would never hurt our son, but the social services got involved and I feared that they may not see it from my point of view. This, plus me not bonding with my son, were the reasons why social services had to get involved.

All these reasons all led to my son going on the Child Protection Register. I was scared that I was going to lose my son. The worse thing I found in my point of view, with the social services was that they intended to use my son as a weapon against me.

Because of that it made me even more determined to get my son off the Child Protection Register. So, therefore, I woke up and I did more for my son no matter how I felt. Even though I didn't love my son at the beginning because I didn't know how to and also it was a case of having to pick him up and having to do things for him. But after my son was about five months the bonding got better and he was able to thrive and be a normal, happy baby. My son got taken off the Child Protection Register when he was six months and I was happy about that.

Once my son reached the age of nine months Rodney died very suddenly of a brain haemorrhage. From this day I am still extremely traumatised by it all as I saw him collapse in his own bathroom and watched him die in hospital. I'm still unable to understand why it happened.

I feel confused but upset for my son as he isn't going to know his father and I'm wondering how my son will take it or even feel let alone understand what really happened. Rodney in my eyes was my soulmate and I loved him.

After Rodney died I'm still unable to explain how I really feel as I'm not ready to grieve just yet. But life without him has been hard. Life is very different for my son and I. Since we have moved to my two-bedroom flat, it's calm, relaxing and close to normality. My son seems happier as I'm not so stressed or as depressed as I was before we moved.

Becoming a mum made me think about my own adoption. It brought back memories such as my son has got everything that he needs and I didn't; he's got love and affection. I remember where one toy was on the shelf, there was a spinning top right on the top shelf on the left-hand side in my orphanage, and I was never allowed to play with it. My son got one for Christmas and it was hard giving it to him to play with. Cots are horrible as well. I don't like my son being in one because of memories of me being in one. He is lucky because he's got everything that he needs and nutrition and things like that.

For the past six months I have been reliving early memories and feelings with my adoption support social worker. The aim is to enable me to bond better with my son, a process which I feel has been successful.

I am still dominated by anger, dreams of deprivation but also driven by high determination which makes me emotionally exceedingly strong inside. Not only have I survived but I am now successful.

SECTION 2

On being adopted

Adoption

Sola (age 11)

Anticipation sparkles through my tender veins as I receive a black book
Disappointment is highly doubted, the front cover has little ladybird
stickers scattered
Opening this welcome book addressed to me from my new mummy
Pictures of a pure white cat beckoned me on the second page
Tickles of my excitement fizz like fireworks around my body
I can't wait to live in the house on the homemade page
Oblivious to the surrounding atmosphere a picture of my new mum on an
Astra car
No doubt of a new happy family

The door to freedom

Kyle (age 12)

I was in a horrible place. This is the door to a happy place.

What I think

Ruby (at age 6)

I think it is special to be adopted because it's exciting to have a new mother and father and sister or brother. I was the only one who was not crying. I was like, 'Who are these people and why am I in their arms? I don't know what's happening to me!' I was really scared, but I didn't cry. When my sisters gave me the toys, I thought you were nice people then. I am fine and happy to be with a new family. It is really cool to be Chinese and English at the same time. That's all!

Ruby (centre) and her sisters sitting on the sofa

Being adopted

Jeremy (age 11)

Being adopted

To be adopted is a really special thing. For instance, you will have the best time of your life with your new parents, you will do lots more things than you used to, and you will have to have some ground rules, like keep the house clean, do your homework, no back chat and don't pull faces at them, do as you're told. Play outside on warm days not coming inside, help your parents pick up stuff, and do family stuff all together.

After school clubs

If you want to do an activity after school just ask them what you can do. You can do whatever activity you want, like football, rugby, tennis, golf, cricket, trampolining, martial arts, athletics, hockey and cross-country running.

Doing things as a family

Sometimes you will have to do things as a family like doing gardening, going food shopping, going on a walk. You can also go on holiday, buy some clothes for you guys; go on a picnic and have a takeaway with your family.

Love is in the air

Henry (age 12)

I was adopted at six-and-a-half and this song is how I felt for about the first two years. Now I feel really happy with my new mummy and daddy.

I can't get close to anyone
It feels like not having any friends
I feel so lonely I have nobody to be with.

love is in the air
love is in the air
I have nobody by my side
love is in the air

I feel like running away
I don't know anyone around me
I feel like a loser

love is in the air
love is in the air
I have nobody by my side
love is in the air

love is in the air
love is in the air
I have nobody by my side
love is in the air

The music is sad and I sing, play the guitar, bass and the guitar solo but Dad has programmed the drums.

Different feelings you feel on being adopted

Jessica (age 9)

Sometimes you feel really scared because you never know if your new parents will be as kind as you want them to be.

Sometimes you'll feel really happy because your old parents were mean to you and you're glad to get a new start to life.

Sometimes it's most scary because you're only young and you are not used to moving.

But you'll always feel a sigh of relief when everything goes really well.

I'm me

Elizabeth (age 17)

What's my identity? I'm me. I am who I am because of everything that's happened to me. Just like anyone else. I'm special because I was "chosen" while other people are just "had". But I'm still the same: I go to school, I take exams, I hang out with my friends, I watch TV, I play ice hockey, I tell awful jokes, I listen to music, I go to parties, and I worry about UCAS applications. I'm the same as everyone else. I'm proud of who I am and where I'm from. It's a part of me. But it doesn't define me.

My happy place

Conor Howard (age 8)

Singing Blue Birds
Happy to fly in the sky.

Shiny Gold Fish
From their bowl watch the world go by.

Old Ginger Toms
In sunshine lie.

I a Baby Black Boy
In the wrong family did often cry.

But here is the right place for me to come
And now I am my Daddy's Son.

Being adopted

Ellie (age 6)

I was nervous because it was my first time being adopted.

My first night with my forever family

Emily Cox (age 8)

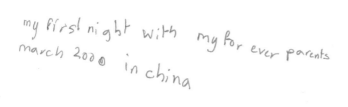

my first night with my for ever parents
march 2000 in china

by emily cox

Being adopted

A B (age 11)

Being adopted is sometimes quite hard because you will never know your birth mum, or if you had a brother or sister back in China, or if your birth mum was married or not. There are loads of things you don't know and probably the most upsetting is not knowing who your birth mum is. You might even pass her in the street but you will never know who she is or how she lived or if she still remembers you.

I'm glad that I was brought into this family; if they hadn't adopted me then who knows what would happen.

I know that it wasn't my birth mum's fault that I was adopted, but she did the best thing for me.

When I am older I would like to go back to China and see the city that I was born in. I know that it's quite unlikely that I will find my birth mum, but if I did I wouldn't know what to do.

When I went to my first school some people in my class started to be racist to me. They started to call me 'flat nose' and other horrible names. When the headmistress didn't do anything about it my mum took me out of that school and put me in another school called Springmead. I have just left the school after five happy years there.

My feelings about adoption

Daniel (age 8)

Adoption isn't that bad because you have a family to look after you.

When my mum and dad told me that I was adopted I was pretty sad but I was glad that I had a brother and sister that loved me.

When me mum started telling me about things that happened when I was living with my birth parents I felt angry.

I wished she had told me sooner but she said that she knew I would get upset so she waited for when I was old enough.

I was having problems at school and my mum and dad were always there and I started to behave.

I'm still not perfect but there's a big change.

Adoption

Muireann (age 10)

Adoption is sad and happy at the same time. You get a new family but you lose one too.

Sometimes you get adopted because your birth family doesn't have enough money or they are too young. I dream about them sometimes. I wonder how they are and if they want to see me. I know I want to see them.

I like the family I have. I was born in Monaghan. I can't really remember what it was like when I was a baby but I know my first family loved me as much as my second family loves me.

I like the school I'm in. I have all my friends there; they are really nice to me.

I have one horse and one pony, two donkeys and a cat. I like animals and they like me.

When I am older I would like to see my birth mother and go shopping with her.

What do adopted young people think about adoption? Here's what!

Chelsey (age 12), Victoria (age 13), Smurfy (age 15) and Mack (age 12)

One adoption agency sent out a questionnaire in 2007 to adopted young people over the age of ten years. Here are some of the responses they received.

What does adoption mean to you?

Having a nice, new loving family. (Chelsey)

Being part of a family. Belonging. Being secure. A fresh start.

Changing your surname. A new beginning. (Smurfy)

Not much. (Mack)

What are the best things about being adopted?

Finding a permanent family that loves you and being able to stay forever. (Smurfy)

Holidays. Parents take care of you. (Mack)

You have someone who really cares for and about you. (Victoria)

You get to meet new people. (Chelsey)

What did you think when you were first told that you were going to be adopted?

I thought it was going to be really terrible because I liked it where I was (with my foster carer). (Victoria)

I wasn't sure what it meant. I thought it would be OK though. (Smurfy)

What did you think when you were first told about your new adoptive family?

I was a bit confused because six months earlier I'd been let down by another adoptive family. I wasn't sure it would work out. But it did! (Smurfy)

I thought it was going to be terrible! (Victoria)

I was really happy. (Chelsey)

What else helped when you were being adopted?

Foster parents and being with other adopted children or children waiting. (Smurfy)

My life story book and having my brother with me. (Mack)

My bear Snowy – I've had him since I was very little. (Victoria)

What is your life story book and why is it important?

It is a book about my life so far. It's important because it helps me understand my past better. (Smurfy)

A life story book has pictures of your old family and things from your past. (Chelsey)

It is a book of my life. I can look back at what I did and see pictures of people. (Mack)

It has my life story in it. It is important to me because it has a lot of memories. (Victoria)

How did your family help you settle into your new home?

They were caring and thoughtful. (Victoria)

By caring about us. Got own bedroom and nice gifts. (Chelsey)

I got my own room and I got to visit my birth dad. (Mack)

They helped me unpack my stuff and tried to get me to know the area better, introduced me to my neighbours who are my age, showed me where my new school was. (Smurfy)

What did you think when you first met your adoptive family? What did you do together?

We went to lunch at my godparents. (Mack)

I thought it wasn't so bad after all. We went strawberry picking and my sister wore the strawberries instead of eating or picking them! (Victoria)

I thought they were crazy but fun. (Chelsey)

I thought they were a bit strange but I found out they were really nice after. We went to the park and had lunch out. We went for a meal at a restaurant. (Smurfy)

Does being adopted ever have an effect on your friendships, at school or elsewhere?

Well, it has done once or twice because a friend's mum singled me out in a group of friends and made some rude comments. (Smurfy)

Sometimes it does. (Chelsey)

Well, not really, but sometime in the future it might. (Victoria)

Would you like to talk to other adopted young people?

Yes I would. It will be helpful because you can let it all out. (Chelsey)

I'm not sure it would be helpful now but I would like to talk to other adopted children about it (it would have been useful at the beginning!). (Smurfy)

Probably. It would help them more than myself I think because they can tell someone with a similar situation to themselves. (Victoria)

Would you like to tell us anything else about being adopted?

Being adopted means if you tell people at school some of the boys may be a bit mean. (Chelsey)

I think being adopted does not matter, so if people make fun of me for being adopted, it does not really matter. (Mack)

There's nothing more to say! (Smurfy)

The Ethiopian experience

Sasha (age 5)

I liked being a baby because I was happy and sad. When I was happy I playing a lot of times and when I was sad I was snuggling into Mummy and it was nice. I liked being a baby and I was not drinking my bottle because I did not like my bottle and I had a nappy. I had a special "blankie" that my aunty gave me and I like to suck it a lot.

I am a big girl now and I want to be really really happy and really really good. I get sad when I think about my birth mother and my birth father and my birth family in Ethiopia because I cannot see them or meet them.

I like being brown and I like being me because I was born in Ethiopia. In my class Abdul is brown, in my class Christina is brown, in my class Ricky is brown, in my class Britoe is brown. All them children make me happy because they are brown like me.

When I go to Ethiopia I am not going to visit my birth mother and my birth father. I feel sad. I cannot wait to get my new baby.

I love my mummy, my daddy and my sister.

Adoption family tree

*Writing by **Luke Howard** (age 10)*

*Drawing by **Conor Howard** (age 8)*

*Colouring by **Milo Howard** (age 7)*

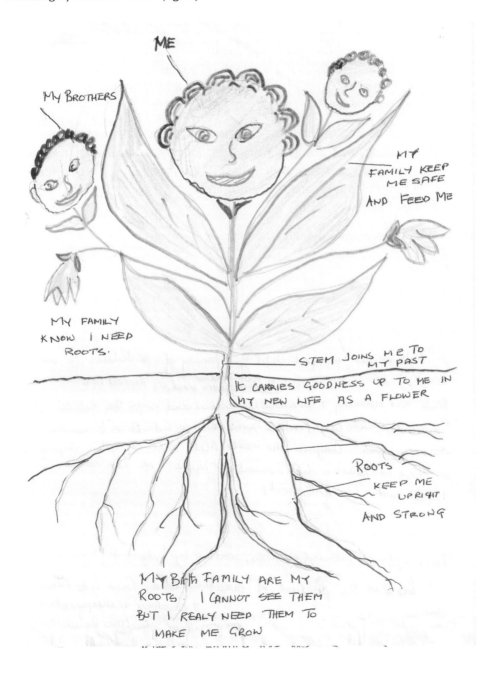

ME

MY BROTHERS

MY
FAMILY KEEP
ME SAFE
AND FEED ME

MY FAMILY
KNOW I NEED
ROOTS.

STEM JOINS ME TO
MY PAST
IT CARRIES GOODNESS UP TO ME IN
MY NEW LIFE AS A FLOWER

ROOTS
KEEP ME
UPRIGHT
AND STRONG

MY BIRTH FAMILY ARE MY
ROOTS. I CANNOT SEE THEM
BUT I REALY NEED THEM TO
MAKE ME GROW

My forever family

Davina (age 11)

Adoption is where you have great fun and meet new people. The best thing is making new friends.

When you are adopted it's really fun and better than anything else in the world. When I moved I was really happy but I didn't *really* know what was happening. You don't when you are that age.

Adopters need to be kind to children. Some parents don't care about children; they don't care about them being adopted. Adopted children are special because they have been through experiences with their [birth] parents, they need care. They can tell their [adoptive] parents about it and if they have got worries they can talk to their [adoptive] parents.

The worse bit is being bullied, bullied about my birthmark.

Adoption

Chantelle (age 12)

Angry at birth parents

Daring to trust new family

Obedience is very hard

Patience is needed

Time is a healer

I need to be helped

Odd feelings are flying

No one can understand me

New family

Chantelle (age 12)

New place, new family, new trust

Everyone tries to understand

What I feel

Feelings can be shown

At any time

Mum and Dad love me loads

I feel lonely sometimes

Love is important

Your family will love you forever

Shock

Elliot (age 11)

On Sunday 18 May 2008 at 11.15am my mum and I had a special talk. My mum said to me, 'I've got to talk to you,' as I always was asking about my dad.

When she called me to talk, I was frightened, curious, wondering what's up: a cold feeling on my skin, butterflies in my stomach.

We sat down in the front room and we looked at each other's eyes. Mum said, 'Elliot, you are my son and I love you very much. I need to talk to you about you; why I'm telling you is you're at an age to understand. Elliot, you didn't come out of my stomach, you came out of someone else's.'

'What!', I said, 'But I look like you!' I was shocked! Confused! It can't be true! You're joking! What's going on?

Tears rolling down my cheeks, I put both hands on my face and cried. My mum hugged me so tight and she started crying.

Am I dreaming? This is a nightmare! I am nobody! Who am I?

Right now, I wish I hadn't been told I am adopted. When my mum told me I was adopted I thought she was joking. I don't know how I feel about being adopted; the shock of having two families. I would like to see photographs of my siblings as I always told my mum I wanted brothers or sisters.

Why? Why? Why?

How did my birth mum feel when she gave me up?

I have so many questions.

Before and after

Adoption and friends – 'I am special'

Jasmine (age 10)

I'm happy, I'm sad other kids make me feel bad
They pick on you because you are "different".
'Where are your brothers or sisters?' they scoff!
'You're lying' they shout!
'You're mum's fake,' they shriek!
Is this because I'm special? . . . Mum and Dad have said I'm special
but I don't always feel it.

BUT WAIT . . . Maybe I am special!
I'm happy, I'm not sad. My adopted friends make me feel glad
They like me, they help me.
They don't ask me personal questions
'Hello Jasmine, are you coming out to play?' they roar!
'Do you need any help?' they ask
They don't make me feel different!
'You're just like us,' they whisper quietly!
Yes, I REALLY am special.

We often get together,
Films, pizzas, parks wherever.
We meet! we eat! we play and talk . . . and parents just chat and chat and
chat!
We might disagree sometimes but we stay friends.
We always look forward to seeing each other.
We always have an exciting day
And that's because we're SPECIAL!!!!

No place like home

Kerri (age 10)

This is a letter I wrote to my new mum and dad when I was feeling sad.

To mummy and daddy

Living here it is like being in a real family. I love being in your family!! I know I annoy you sometimes and I get a bit annoyed with you. I just want you to know I love you and always will!

Thank you for always trying to adopt us so many times but I am so glad we can now be together forever. When I am old enough to live on my own I will know and I am sure you will know there is no place like home! No one could ever replace you two in the world!

From your little one,

Kerri

Lessons learnt or hearts burnt?

David Joel Helliwell (age 19)

Where do I belong? Obviously I have a family,
I have known no other mother.
The other got lost on the rollercoaster of life.
Lost in her own strife.
Lessons learnt or hearts burnt?
A mother's head turned but not to me and her.

Ignorance is bliss till someone tells you this:
'You have a sister'
All my life wondering where my blood ties lie
Yet I cannot see a sister with even my mind's eye.
My life is changing every day my family say.

They try yet they do not know how my emotions flow
One tangent to the next.
What has been, what will be
None can think but me.

Going to a multi-cultural school

Joshua (age 12)

Last summer I started at my new secondary school in northwest London. At first I was very nervous but I settled in and I now enjoy my school. I was worried about getting used to it and about getting bullied. Now that I've settled in though I'm very happy and I haven't been bullied once, although I've seen other people been called names, e.g. gay boy (they're not gay, it's an insult) and spastic. Although I've seen bullying and a bit of racism around me, I feel happy to be going to a multi-cultural school and I am happy to have people around me who look like me and people who are from Asia too.

My class is very mixed like most of the forms in my year. We have a kid from Iraq and Afghanistan, a few kids are from Kosovo, one from Germany, some from Pakistan and Vietnam, two from Nigeria and a few who are white English. I have quite a few Asian kids in my class so I don't feel an outsider. It makes me feel good because there are lots of kids who are Asian and who have the same skin colour as me.

Going to a multi-cultural school makes me feel like I belong due to my skin colour and where I come from. I feel happy to be Thai and although there aren't any other Thai kids that I know at the school, there are lots of people who come from near Thailand. I feel happy about my colour as the majority of children are brown-skinned children. In fact, it's really cool to be my colour.

What it's like being adopted

Katie (age 9)

Katie and her (adoptive) mum discussed these questions. The answers are Katie's exact words.

What are your favourite things?

My favourite things are Horses, Unicorns, John, Shannon, Ewan, Lewis and Ellie (the adoption gang), my mum and my dad and Cleo and Duchess (the pets) of course!

What can you remember about before you came to us?

She tried to look after me but I think she wasn't ready for it.

Do you sometimes think about your tummy mummy? What sorts of things do you think?

I do think about her but I don't know much information about her – but she tried to look after me but didn't succeed and gave me away to the adoption people.

Can you remember the first time you met me and your dad? What do you remember about it?

They met me on my second birthday and I had a really nice day and they played with me all day and they were really kind and sweet.

What are the best things about being adopted?

We have an adoption group (John, Shannon Ellie, Ewan and Lewis) and we always meet up and play and also I have a nice school with lots of friends – my best friends at school are Ella, Nikita and Crystal – oh and Lydia.

What are the worst things about being adopted?

The worst thing about being adopted is when you are taken away from your mum young and it's good that you are adopted but you want to know about your real mum as you don't know anything about her.

How do you feel about being adopted?

Quite happy 'cos I have a loving family and I have two pets that love me lots.

What do you feel about yourself? Who are you?

I feel like I was someone else sometimes.

What do you like about yourself?

I like myself because I know if I hurt myself I have my mummy to help me and she will always look after me and Cleo (my dog) will always lick me.

What would you change?

I would probably change the rating of when you can't see your mum till your 18 as she might have moved and you can't find her and it ends up a horrible mess – you should be able to see her whenever you want.

Are there times when you feel happy and times when you feel sad? When are they?

I feel happy when it's my birthday but I also feel sad as I think she should have been there and she can't because of the 18 years old rating.

I feel happy when I am with my adoption gang.

Making sense of adoption . . . How do you sort things out in your mind about being adopted?

I just try and forget that I am adopted and I am just a normal kid and try to have a normal life.

What help have you received?

From my family – by them not acting if I am really special and not being spoilt, getting told off and getting pocket money and normal things like that.

Who do you talk to about adoption?

I talk to my mum and dad as I know they understand me and I tell little adoption secrets to my dog as I know she won't tell.

Is there anything else you would like to know?

Information about my mum – my tummy mum – what she looks like, what's her name and things like that.

Is there anything else you don't understand?

I don't understand why people can't see their mum until they are 18 and they are a proper lady.

As you know we have always kept in touch with Auntie Steph's family (John, Shannon and Ellie) and Auntie Deb's family (Ewan and Lewis) who adopted around the same time as us. What is it like meeting up with these families?

It is really fun as me and John were adopted first and then Ewan came and then Lewis and then Shannon and Ellie – but I have most fun with John as he was there first.

What things do you do?

We play just like normal kids – we have fun and we don't think of ourselves as adopted.

What are the good things?

They are just children who I can have fun with – they just need a friend who has the same problem.

What things don't you like?

I don't like it when we argue as it is always like older kids versus younger kids or girls versus boys and in the end something breaks.

And there is the larger support group that is arranged by social services where we have big days out and Christmas parties, etc.

I like it because they have music and bouncy castles. I like the social workers who come as they are kind and are like family too.

What could be done to help adopted children?

It could be good if they had little parties so that social workers can answer things like 'What's your mum's name?' and they can say things like 'Your mum is called Kerry,' from their list.

Katie – do you want to add anything or say anything else?

I would like to say that I enjoy being adopted and I like it and I hope everyone can adopt like my mummy and daddy – my mummy is called Deborah and my daddy is called Patrick and my little dog is called Cleo. I love her and she makes me laugh. I think all adopted kids should have a pet and they are busy loving and caring for it and they forget they are adopted and think that they are like other normal kids. I would recommend they don't pick a fish. I recommend they pick a dog as they are cute and cuddly and they always make you laugh.

Thank you Katie . . .

I'm not finished yet!

Everyone should have fun with their parents as they just want the best for you and my mummy and daddy love me but I think you need some more info about why your tummy mummy and daddy couldn't handle you and just give up – well, not all of them give up. I want to know more of what the social workers know that my mummy doesn't know. If I could recommend a type of dog I would recommend a border terrier as they are loyal and they never feel down – a man would be proud to walk it and it goes on your lap, too, for women. And she is a good playmate.

This has been Katie and my dog Cleo who I love very much.

Thank you Katie!

An extra secret life

Heather (Nan Ziyuan) Macrae (age 11)

Being adopted means you have a special secret life that no one who's not adopted can have.

The easiest way to explain what I mean is this. Everyone has a bit of themselves that everyone knows – how smart they are, their behaviour, their usual temper, their talents and their hobbies. This bit is their outside bit, their important life. Everybody also has secret inside important lives. People's secret emotions live there, which we don't tell anyone about, like how we really feel about someone or something, and include secret acts when we do something, but don't tell anyone what we have done. Sometimes the biggest secret life is when people get a chance at whole new lives where we can act, behave, and show different talents or hobbies in a very different way. Going to senior school will be a bit like this.

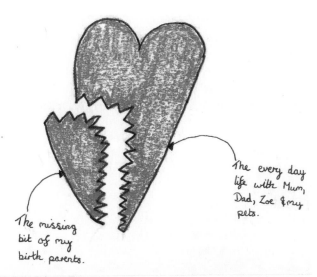

The every day life with Mum, Dad, Zoe & my pets.

The missing bit of my birth parents.

I find being adopted really hard, but I get on with my every day life. The bit of heart is what I try to put behind me.

Broken heart

My family

Ayesha (age 10)

My family is always inside me,

They wash and clean me, feed me and more,

I hope one day my birth parents would . . .

Come to my house and knock on my door.

But what my heart is telling me,

Is to stick with this FAMILY!

I love my family they are the best,

My sister is a little annoying,

She is also a pest but of course she is one of the best.

My brother is really crazy,

Every time I play with him I need a rest,

And I get really lazy.

Let's go on to mum and dad,

Well, when I'm feeling lonely and sad,

There's always DAD.

And when I have got an empty tummy,

Who do I go to: MUMMY.

There is one more thing I forgot to tell you,

I have the most cuddliest, prettiest cat alive.

Guess who that is?

It's JESS!

Home

Alison (at age 12)

Home is where my Mother is
Home is where my Father is
Home is where my sisters are
Home is where my dogs are.

Home is humble
Just a house
A place to call your own.

Home is where my Mother is
Home is where my Father is
Home is where my sisters are
Home is where my dogs are.

Home is the safest place to be
Home means the world to me.

My feelings

Phan Thi Mỹ Liên (age 7)

I wish I was the same colour as my family. It would not matter if my family had any colour skin, it would just be nice to be the same colour. I would have liked to be born to my mummy and daddy, most of the time it is hard to be different.

Home and my heart

Zoe (Lin Xiuji) Macrae (age 6)

I feel happy because I love my mum and dad, my sister and my pets. I feel sad because my birth mother left me. We go on holiday to China every year because we come from there. I am excited going to China; I like to play in the parks there. I like the food and the beds there. But best of all I like the beds at home.

Different!

Nathan Glazier (age 12)

Being adopted isn't all that bad,
You may be different, but just a tad.

You get new parents they love you a lot.
They look after you, from sometimes a tot!

Brothers and sisters you sometimes get
They'll like you a lot, oh yes I'll bet!

Being adopted isn't all that bad,
You may be different, but just a tad.

LOVE!!

Nathan Glazier (age 12)

At first I was worried
At first I was scared
But then I noticed
The love that they shared

They welcomed me in
To their wonderful life
With his name Gary
And Hayley his wife

They gave me comfort
Soon I forgot the past
They gave me love
That would always last

And that's why I love them
My mum and dad
Cause they are the best parents
That I've ever had!

Adoption

Rebecca Glazier (age 11)

Being adopted is great because you know who you are with a family who cares for you and loves you very much. I know it may be hard to leave your parents but you know they can't look after you, but they can write to you and they will always love you.

A new start

Harriet (age 11)

I am with a good new family. We do great things together like going on outings. I feel happier and safer because I know that Mum and Dad are always there for me. I still feel homesick when I am away from my forever mum and dad but I know that's alright. I am glad that I get to see my other sister so I can see her grow up.

Why is it important for brothers and sisters to go to the same adoptive family?

Claire (age 12)

Because some parents might not know how the children feel and they can talk about it to each other.

If they are split up it would be bad because they have already been split up from friends and family and it would hurt to be split up from more people.

Children are really close to family so if they have been separated they could think about sad stuff all the time and never be happy and they've already been split from someone so it would be bad to be split from someone else.

Why is it important for brothers and sisters to go to the same adoptive family?

Claire (age 12)

We can choose whether we talk to each other about being adopted or not. Some children might not want to ever talk about it. Others may only want to talk about it to family. Others may want to tell everyone. BUT IT'S NOTHING TO BE ASHAMED OF!!!!!!

Being put with my sisters is great because if any of us are worried or upset the others can make her feel better.

A great new life

Davina (age 11)

We have great holidays. I get to see my sister which is great. I love school to bits because of the teachers who teach us things. Our new family look after us really, really well, it's awesome. I have lots of friends and do lots of different things that I enjoy.

Adoption poem

Samantha (age 12)

Adoption – a new beginning

A new life

I venture to my new home

Everything will change

My family the best I've had

My dream come true

Love, care, happiness enters my heart

A child made happy just by adopting

A child to care for

A child to love

A life made different and new

Every child is special

Julia (at age 14)

I was adopted when I was small. I lived with a foster family for a short while. I have contact with my eldest sister by letter. She sounds so lovely and when I am older I may meet her. I have more birth sisters but have no contact with them. I would like to though. I am the youngest child in my birth family, but the eldest in the family I have now . . . my forever family.

I love playing sport and being with my friends who I love and miss a lot when I am away from school. I love my school and my family and I have amazing friends, some of which are older than me. All my friends are so lovely and sometimes when things are not so great I talk to them. Obviously everyone feels sad in their lives, even a non-adopted person, and it's really important you can talk to someone you trust about how you feel.

I am glad I am adopted, although adoption brings with it feelings of loss, sadness, anger and many, many more feelings it also brings great joy and happiness to everyone involved. My parents were given a chance to have a child they otherwise couldn't have, my biological parents tried to rebuild their lives and I was given a second chance to have a happier life. I would like to say thank you to my family for adopting me and for being the best ever. I love them so much. They have changed my life so much for the better, I could never describe how much.

When I am older maybe when I am a granny, after I have been a policewoman and a mummy and a sailing instructor for disabled children, I would like to be a foster mum and be able to give other children another chance in life like I was given. I think it is a lovely thing to do as children also have feelings which are valid and should be recognised and every child deserves to be loved no matter who they are or what they are like. Every child is special and worth something in the world.

I am adopted

Oisin Ruslan (age 5)

I'm glad to be in Ireland with my mam and dad and brother. I am very special and my name is Oisin. I am very happy to be adopted. I miss my mam and dad in Russia. I wonder, have I brothers or sisters in Russia? I would like to visit Russia some time.

Adoption

Kyle (age 12)

Adoption improves your life.

The magic of a mother's kiss

Anita Nitiluk Hennessy (age 14)

Every time I feel afraid
I say a little Prayer,
I look around instinctively
My Mother standing there,
She puts her arms around me
With a kiss she dries my tears,
The lovely words she says to me
Dispels my many fears.

At night as I lie in bed,
Trying to go to sleep,
Each noise I hear frightens me
And through my fingers I do peep.
In the clouds the thunder claps,
The lightning lights the sky,
There but for my Mother
I would surely die.

When we go walking in the park,
I stumble, then I fall.
My body aching all over
For my Mother again I call,
She comes to my assistance
My life with her is bliss,
Now I really understand
THE MAGIC OF A MOTHER'S KISS.

A poem for my mum

George (at age 20)

My sky changed from black to blue

The day I came to live with you,

I was lost, like moving sand

No more, because I am found,

From day one you treated me like your own son

I am proud to call you mum

Adoption feelings

Michael (at age 10)

Good feelings about adoption

My mum and dad say I'm special.
They feel proud of me.
I feel proud of them.
It is good to know there are others who are adopted.
Sometimes you think about your birth family and wonder what they would have been like.
Sometimes you might be scared about what's happening.
Sometimes you might be confused.
Memories are important.

"Special" means

different from other children with more mums and dads.
It is important to know why I can't live with my birth family.
I think about age seven or eight is the right time to know that you're adopted.
It's important for children to ask about themselves.
It makes you excited being able to explore and find things out about your birth family.
It is important to know about other relatives.
It is nice to have new relatives.

Hard things

If you are older when you go to live with your adoptive family you would remember more about your birth family and you could be sad.
You might have to change school.

Bad feelings about adoption

Devastated
Sad
Scared
Lonely

Heather's heart

Heather (Nan Ziyuan) Macrae (at age 8)

Broken heart

Yummy yummy gummy

Sola (age 11)

Adoption is like a packet of gummy bears
Some people only like the black
Whereas others hate the green bears
Others prefer the reds to the oranges
But the rest stick to yellow

A packet of gummy bears is like adoption
Some people only like working in a children's home
Whereas others hate the thought of lots of parentless children
Others prefer the younger children to the older
But the rest stick to teenagers

Adoption is like a packet of gummy bears
Some people like working in foster homes
Whereas other hate the thought of only helping one kid at a time
Others prefer babies to toddlers
But the rest stick with youngsters

A packet of gummy bears is like adoption
Some people like adopting many many children
Whereas others hate adopting full stop
Others prefer to adopt siblings to half siblings
But the rest stick to one

Adopting is like a packet of gummy bears
Some children only like the different people
Whereas others hate all the moving
Others prefer to try all their options to choosing straight away
But the rest stick to one family

A packet of gummy bears is like adopting
Some children only like a mum and dad
Whereas others hate the idea of a dad
Others prefer to have adoptive brothers to adoptive sisters
But the rest stick to a single child

Adopting is like a packet of gummy bears
Some people only like the black
Whereas others hate the green bears
Others prefer the red bears to the oranges
But the rest stick to the yellows

Happiness

Jason (at age 7)

Happiness smells like chocolate,

Happiness is my Mum and Dad,

Happiness makes me bounce up and down,

Happiness makes me wash up,

Happiness makes me play,

Happiness sounds like clapping, cheering and stamping,

Happiness is fun and laughter.

Becoming a baby

Charlene Stagles (at age 11)

Can I see your baby when it is born?

Can Rachel walk and talk?

I became a baby when I was nearly four years old,

That was when I was thinking about walking and talking.

I would like to be a baby in my mummy's tummy,

So she can talk to me, and it would be all cosy.

Postscript: 'Becoming a baby' was written for a lady who was expecting her second baby. Rachel was the first child. Charlene walked on her own unexpectedly at the age of five in mainstream nursery and started talking when she was seven.

Lucky?!

Amy (age 17)

When people used to say I was lucky I didn't believe them,
They said I was lucky for being chosen,
They said I was lucky for being rescued,
They said I was lucky for all those different people loving me.

I just used to say I'm not lucky you are,
They are lucky for having both parents,
They are lucky for knowing their parents,
They are lucky for being loved by THEIR parents.

I wasn't lucky because if I was lucky I wouldn't have got in trouble with the police,
If I was lucky I wouldn't have got in with the wrong crowd,
If I was lucky I wouldn't have been on drugs,
If I was lucky I wouldn't have lost some of my closest mates.

I was lucky to have two different families,
I'm lucky because I was chosen,
I'm lucky because my best friend and fiançé listened to my problems,
I'm lucky because I have new and much closer mates,
I'm lucky because I've been rescued all my life.

I'm lucky because I MADE me lucky!

SECTION 3

On being apart

To mum poem

Rosie (age 5, with the help of her brother, Rowan, age 9)

I love you too much and I want to see you I wish I can find you 'cause I want to see you

I hope you get this message I hope you get this message I hope you have the keys

To let me in your flat

I don't know where you are Ireland or England or even Australia I don't have a clue

I hope you're feeling better I hope you get this letter I hope you get this letter

I hope you get this message I hope you get this message I hope you have the keys

To let me in your flat

From Rosie

Questions for 'tummy mummy'

Karen Ulyana Roche (age 7)

To my tummy mummy

I would like to know a few questions

I would like to know do I have any brothers or sisters?

I am seven years old now

I go to Scoil Mhuire

I would like to know what my daddy's name is

I would like to know what colour your eyes are

My hair is blond

I would like to know where you live in Russia

I would like to know why I was adopted.

How I feel about my birth mother

Marisa Midian Lucero (age 8)

I miss Sofía because I hardly ever see her and because she lives in Guatemala. When I think about her, sometimes I cry. I love her because she gave me my name, Lucero, which means bright shining star in Spanish. I think that every time she looks up at the stars she thinks of me.

Toucan
by marisa
age 7

Adoption

K B (age 9)

I find it hard because I'm sad. I'm sad because I miss my birth mum.

Sometimes I wonder if my birth mum knew me. That I am in England? One day I would like to go back to China and look at my orphanage. It's sad when you be adopted.

Adoption is nice
Adoption is sad
Adoption makes me glad
And sometimes mad.

My thoughts . . .

Kevin Toni Mitchell (at age 18)

My thoughts cannot escape her

My eyes search for her face

My life is running to her

My heart hurts with the pace

My dreams centre around her

My sleep is her domain

My wish is to be with her

My love can't be restrained

My doubt tells me I'm foolish

My reason knows the truth

My heart tells me she loved me

My pictures are the proof

My time is spent in waiting

My life has still to start

My dream is to belong once more

Then never be apart

I always wonder

Fiona Higham (at age 17)

I have never met my birth mother or father. My family have always been open about the adoption. I know a little about my real mum and dad and sometimes have so many questions, but feel I can't ask them. I try to forget about that stage in my life, but sometimes it is impossible. I just think it doesn't matter, but it has influenced me as a person for the whole of my life and I know it will carry on doing so.

Sometimes I feel as if there is a big hole missing in my life. I feel I don't fit it. I don't feel normal. I have a whole different life somewhere else. I feel I am two different people. Half of me is Kelly Marie Hutchinson and the other is Fiona Mary Anne Higham. I don't know which one I belong to.

I sometimes pretend I am no one at all and no one knows me. That way I don't have to face who I really am.

I love meeting new people because I can tell them what I want them to hear. It is easier than the truth.

I do love my mum and dad but because they know me so well I try to stay away from them for fear that they will tell people who I really am; which in their eyes is an adopted teenager with many problems. There is more to me than that.

I wish I was like everyone else, but I am not and I need to accept that and get on with my life.

I never feel happy in anything I do. Sometimes I feel like a failure. I don't feel wanted – this is because my real mum didn't want me. I think to myself what is wrong with me, why me?

I want to be happy with myself, but how?

Can I be like everyone else?

Can Fiona take over the whole of me one day and make me the person I have longed to be?

Can I actually be proud of myself? Can I stop putting on an act?

I wait for this day like I wait for the day I will get married. I know deep down it will come.

I am not a bad person, I just have some horrible feelings sometimes and I run away from them instead of facing them. When I face these horrible feelings I will become a new person.

I always wonder about what my real mum looks like now and does she look like me?

Does she remember me? Does she think about me on my birthday? Has she told my other brothers and sisters about me? All of these questions no one can answer. Where am I supposed to put all these feelings inside me? I can't ignore them. They always seem to be at the back of my mind.

I don't mean to hurt people; I just find it hard to accept responsibility for my actions.

I don't blame this on the adoption, I blame this on the feelings I have inside.

I know I take after my real mum in the fact that I am likeable and friendly, with a good sense of humour. I do think about her and I hope she thinks about me. She is a memory and maybe one day the memory will become reality.

At the end of the day she is my mum and I am her daughter. I can never forget that.

Untitled Rap

Leon "City" Davis (age 19)

This here a callin a brother in mournin

torn from those you are born to be with

over something I had no control of ****

I love 'em like my own kids

Mum's disowned me I was her first kid

that hurts deep why didn't she love me but believe hate takes too much

energy

as long as you remember me and when you're ready

know I'll still be here I shed tears the first in years

When my mum come downstairs how do you prepare

someone you love as your own tell him he can't go back to the place he

called home

If I could I would clap her 'dome' with da 'chrome'

but for my brothers I don't

For you I will grow become a person you look up to not a stat sellin 'coke'

Jade I wish you knew what I know whatever you say, feel or do we're still

going to be bros

even after years you decide you want to know pick up da phone

to all my true fams my home's your home

how was I to know I'd remind her of my pups

I'm sorry I wasn't white enough

For 17 years it's not like she had time to influence my life too much

I was wrong to trust my instincts in this incident now it's left me in a predicament one bro don't give a **** da other two probably too young to understand it branded a black sheep, this black G battered and bruised mentally but still ever ready like batteries battling the pain and agony that cuts deep my thanks to the family the tragedy started about day three

Since then it's never ceased forever become a beast never will I be at peace but started pickin up the pieces by pickin up pieces making money off a weed developed my 16s till there sickly hog the light cos I'm greedy put out my first CD fingers crossed my bros will rate me and the nation will pay me so I'm able to take care of your worries

J Ruuf and Leev I will always love you

© Leon Davis 2008

When words aren't enough

Kevin Toni Mitchell (at age 18)

I can't find the words

They do not exist

No sentence or song

Could say how you were missed

The pain didn't end

I sleep without rest

Mortally wounded

Though healthy in flesh

I cry with dry eyes

I ran out of tears

I still scream within

But no one can hear

Detached and dispatched

Adrift and alone

I live in a house

But have not a home

The mother for whom

I've so long yearned

Loved, left and never returned.

My faith, our bond, my heart

All broken

But words won't suffice

They are pointlessly spoken

My birth mum

Solome (age 8)

This is what I think my birth mum looks like. I got collected when I was five months old. My mum and dad are very nice. I think my mum was pretty.

Shall I think of you?

Kevin Toni Mitchell (at age 18)

Shall I think of you in years to come

When all I have sought to do is done?

When I have succeeded, when I am complete

When I have a nice house on a well-to-do street

When the "good life" is mine and I live it unfettered

When I feel as though things could hardly be better

I'd take stock of it all, then my smile disappears

As I think of all that you've missed through the years

Head hung low I'd sit back and sigh

But what can be done? The bygones have gone by.

If I could go back what words could I find

To borrow your ears, try change your mind?

How would I say it, where would I start?

What words could convey the want in my heart?

Pictures speak a thousand words

I looked at our photos, listened and heard

Your eyes speak volumes of what's clear to see

The love that you once had only for me

You made your decision and though broken hearted

You signed on the line and so we were parted

Shall I think of you in years to come

When all I have sought to do is done?

I know this sounds foolish, of this I am sure

For all of my wealth I would remain poor

My wretched heart still destitute

With a labour of love that bears no fruit

I wonder sometimes, will it always be such

that I have a great deal, but never enough.

Time goes by, the years they pass

people change but feelings last.

You might never know if I weren't to say

The truth is I think of you everyday

A wish too great to be said aloud

Is that one day we'd meet and you would be proud

SECTION 4

Staying in touch

Contact is really important

Georgie *(age 11)*

My sister and I are allowed to write a letter to our mum every year. When the time comes to write it is very exciting. We write about all our news. I love the day we get a letter back from our mum. I feel very excited waiting for the letter. It's a shame we only get to write once a year because I have lots of news I could tell my mum. I only get to write once a year because the judge said so. I think the judge's decision that we can't meet until I am an adult was a good idea. If I did meet her it would mix with my life now and make my life complicated and make me feel pulled in two directions.

We are allowed to meet our brother. I get to see him once or twice a year because we live in different countries. I love seeing him. I feel very happy and excited when we are going to meet. It's like seeing a long lost friend. I love the excitement of meeting him at the door. When we are together we go to the park, to the shops or to the cinema. Mostly we just play games like spies or pirates. We all sleep in the same room and play a game where we have to roll over each other – it keeps us awake for hours. I hate leaving or seeing him leave but there is always the chance that our parents will get distracted and we get another half an hour together. I miss my brother but I don't cry. We phone each other quite often. My sister always pulls faces when I am on the phone to him because she wants me to finish so she can have a chat.

I feel contact is really important. There's no point in hiding the fact that you have another mother in the world because some day you'll meet her again. It's important to know about her and what she is doing. It's important not to hide your emotions because if you do some day they will all come out together and you might feel depressed.

I don't have contact with my dad. I never knew him – I can't remember him. I didn't even see a photo of him until I was nine. I asked my mum if she had a photo and she got in touch with him and got me two photos. Seeing the photos didn't really have a big effect on me. I was curious to see what he looked like and to see if he looked like me. I was a little disappointed that we didn't look like each other. I wonder if my dad is in any way like me in personality. I would like to get in touch with him – maybe a letter each year.

I think some of the other people in my past life weren't the nicest people so I don't want them to have anything to do with me again or to have them in my life.

If I was given a choice about contact I would find it very tricky. I'd love to meet my mum but then it would be scary because I'd feel torn. It's a difficult thing to think about and I have no idea what I would decide if I was given the choice. I think different things different days.

I think life is nicer and easier for me because my mum and my parents are in contact too. They write letters to each other. My parents think my mum is a very nice person. If they didn't write I'd feel upset because I'd think that they didn't like each other and were jealous of each other. My parents met my mum and we have a photo of them together. I think both my mums will be great friends when we meet again.

Contact

Millie (age 10)

The word contact means when you get in touch with someone. I have contact with my brother and my mum.

I have contact with my mum every year. I write to her near the summertime. I like to write to her. Contact means something to me. Writing to my mum makes me feel happy and stops me from feeling lonesome. I'm not allowed to see her until I'm 18. The judge decided that we couldn't see her. At the start I felt it wasn't fair that I couldn't see her until I was 18 and it made me annoyed and cross but then I realised that 18 was OK. It's eight years more until I see her because I'm only ten now. It's just eight more years really. I feel it's not that long away. When I was six I used to cry a lot and miss her and 18 seemed too far away. I can't see her because I might want to stay with her when I'd have to leave. But if I did stay I'd miss my other parents. My sister has seven more years until she's 18 so she will be able to see her before me.

When I'm doing my contact I think a lot. I choose good pictures for my mum. I feel nice choosing photos – it shows her how I'm growing up. It's nice to think about my mum and get letters from her. When I was younger I didn't know how to write letters so I would tell my mummy or daddy what I wanted to say and they would write it out so that I could copy it. I feel happy when I post it – not sad. I blow kisses and hugs into the envelope before I close it. I like it when she sends me back letters. She sends me photos of my baby brother. He wasn't adopted. I haven't ever met him but my dream is to meet him some day. All this is really nice for me. There's nothing better than this for me and my mum.

I can get in touch with my brother anytime. He was adopted by another family. I like visiting him in England and sleeping over with him and playing with him. We have lots of fun and mess and jump on the beds like lunatics. When I see him it makes me feel really happy. And when I leave it kind of makes me feel sad. I talk to him on the phone a lot. For my birthday I got a Roald Dahl DVD from him – it was good and the stories were funny.

I would like to have contact with my father. I haven't seen him and he won't know how much I've grown up. When I'm an adult he might not even remember me. I think he might have taken care of me when I was a baby because I saw a photo of us but he never lived with me because he had another family. If I could change a thing I would tell the judge to make my father get a photo of me so that my stepbrother and stepsister could see me. But the rule can't be changed.

Contact is important for me because if I didn't have it I couldn't talk to my mum in letters.

Let us make our own mind

Marcus Wootton-Kahn *(age 20)*

When I was still fostered I saw my birth mother quite a bit but I didn't like it. She would say things that I didn't want to hear. I also saw my nanny which I liked.

Since I've been adopted I see my birth mother once a year. My mum and birth mother and me have a meal together and I am happy with that.

I still see my birth family nanny four times a year and I enjoy that.

Social workers should not force children to see birth relatives they don't want to see and let them make their own mind up.

Her

Julia (at age 14)

She stares at me I'm centre of her world,

She has one thing on her mind, that's me,

That's all she can see, I assume all she thinks of,

Those eyes so warm just smiling twinkling in the sun,

She is staring out at the unknown, that's me,

She is meant to know me but doesn't, through no fault of hers,

Despite that, she continues to look at me and all my flaws,

Her mouth undisturbed, her nose the same her hair a little darker,

Whenever I look she's looking, at me but no one else,

I try talking, sometimes shout but she never answers,

It hurts but I know why,

For here in front of me is a person real yet not,

The real person thinks a lot and sees most things but me,

For in front of me is her face, but not in flesh, but in a small horizontal frame I keep close to my heart.

The letter

Julia (at age 14)

The letterbox opened and out it flew,

Before I had opened it I knew it was from you,

The whiz of excitement as I read what you say,

This is by far the highlight of my day,

First I feel excited then I feel sad,

Angry, confused, overjoyed and then mad,

I wish I could hug you and catch up on lost time,

To be taken away from you was such a crime,

I know I don't know you, but from your letters I feel I do,

All that matters is our relationship just me and you,

I am glad I was adopted it gave me a new chance,

To be alive to be free to sing and dance,

I can't wait to see you, that day will be great,

A day full of happiness not full of hate,

One day we will meet up, the two of us together,

We will hug and talk and I will love you forever.

My sister's new parents won't let me see her

Sola (age 11)

When your life comes to a halt, and starts to spin the other way,
Not all of your problems get solved in a day.
In fact these things take weeks, months, even years
So if you are young and find it hard to understand
We like to be told in a way we are familiar with.
A story about a chicken or a bird would help
About how it had to move on due to ill parenting.
Also a monthly checkup when in a foster home –
A visit to the current bedroom
The social worker to think what it would be like to have a room like that
I remember when I was in care my room only had a set of Disney books,
And one big teddy,
I look back and think how I would have liked something else in there too.
Wouldn't you?

I wish social workers could make a law
A law that says any siblings who get split up HAVE to have at least one
visit a year
If split up from one another
Because I am in an experience where nothing and nobody can stop my
sister's parents from stopping her from seeing me
I have only seen my sister twice in six years away from her.

I also wish that when put into care that you could: share a room, with
whom you like,
All have the right amount of pocket money,
Have a monthly shopping trip
And also eat chocolate for breakfast, lunch and dinner!

Broken contact – broken heart

Sola (age 12)

SECTION 5

Revisiting my birth place

Past and present

Josephine Chunrui Jay (at age 9)

An unwanted daughter
From the rice fields of China
Born across to the land of rain
Raised by parents,
Loving and true
Never prone to seek the spotlight
Nor the teacher's empty words
Skilled with pen
From tutor of father
Along with brush
Only time can tell.

Returned to the land of rice
To see the finder's stone
Outside the walls of the forbidden city
Once barred to many
And on the boundaries tall.

Back to the home once protecting
Then to the orphanage who covered my head
And swathed me in many blankets
For the return to the land of rain.

So I am a Cockney

Luke Howard (at age 9)

When I was six years old I wrote a poem which was chosen to be printed in a book. When the book was ready there was a special party in London and I was invited to go. I was excited to be meeting other people who had written for the book, but most of all I wanted to go to London because I was born there.

We got a train from home and when we arrived at the station in London we soon got a taxi. Mum told the driver I needed to see all the special London sights as this was my first visit since I was collected from Guy's Hospital only one day old and taken to live in the West Country.

The man was very interesting as we drove around he told me about the streets and buildings that I had only seen on television. He took me to see Buckingham Palace and talked about the history of so many things.

After a while I saw the Parliament building with Big Ben, behind I could see the London Eye and the driver stopped the taxi on the bridge over the Thames and pointed to a tall building and said, 'Welcome home lad, that is where you were born, Guy's.'

It made me feel funny to think that is where I was first of all and here I am back again in London seeing it all!

We got out of the taxi right by a stall selling London toys and caps, my mum thanked the driver for his help and got money to pay him, but he shook his head and smiled at me and said he was 'proud to welcome a Cockney home'.

Visiting Vietnam

Phan Thi Mỹ Liên (age 7)

In the summer my family and I went to Vietnam for a three-week holiday. The best parts about the holiday were swimming, playing on the beach with my friends and riding cyclos. Cyclos are bikes with a seat on the front for a passenger.

We spent some of our time in Ho Chi Minh City, which is very big and busy and is where I was born. We also spent time in Hoi An, which is a lovely town by the sea. In Hoi An we met our friends from England; they were born in Vietnam too.

All the girls in Vietnam looked like me. That made me feel nervous. I made friends with some of the ladies working in the hotel, they were friendly and I enjoyed spending time with them.

My mum and dad met a girl called Phuong nine years ago when they adopted my brother. She is 17 now and sells books to tourists, I bought lots of Harry Potter books from her. She is a very happy smiley person, she played cards with me and I really enjoyed spending time with her.

One day we took a van ride to the outskirts of Ho Chi Minh City to see Sister Hai. She was in charge of the children's home when me and my brother were there. Sister Hai now runs 'The House of Love', which is a nursery for the babies of ladies without husbands. This means the mothers can go to work and keep their babies. Next we went around the corner to visit the children's home, where I stayed for seven weeks when I was a baby. I saw a lot of children, most of them were babies and toddlers and there were some older children.

When we left Vietnam I cried because I had such a lovely time there that I didn't want to leave. We are going back in two years time. I would like to go back next year but we have to save up our money. It was a shame we couldn't stay longer.

Phan Thi Mỹ Liên with Phuong, Vietnam

Me and my China

Ruby (age 7)

Before

I am looking forward to seeing the other babies who are now in the orphanage. I'm going to be glad to see the ladies who looked after me. I want to get some jade. I want to remember my China trip.

During

It is wonderful to be in China. Because it has loads of nice people. And food. I might like it too much and want to stay, but Mum says don't worry, we'll come back again to visit. I like going down the Great Wall on a lift like yesterday, there are lots of fun things.

After

I liked being in China. I am glad I went to see it all again, it made me think of when I was there before. It was sort of helpful to see it all and fun to be in China. And not helpful as some of it reminded me of when I didn't have a mummy and daddy. But I got some jade and I want to go back another time. I liked going. I miss China.

Vietnam

Lê Văn Thanh (age 10)

One of the best things about Vietnam is all the different types of transport, like motorbikes, cyclos and boats. The very best thing is that the owners are happy to let me drive. In England there are too many rules about driving under age.

Văn Thanh going out for hotel kitchen supplies, Hoi Chi Minh City, 2007

Visiting my roots (Romania)

Terezia Dziubak (age 20)

I know vital knowledge about my background. I was three-and-a-half when I joined my adoptive family; I was placed in an orphanage in Satu-Mare in Romania from birth in 1987. I was adopted by a British couple and I moved to England in 1991.

I think it was during my two sisters' adoption, when my adoptive parents decided to take the adoption to court, the court as far as I know recommended that we go to Romania, and to go and see my biological parents and siblings.

I remember quite clearly before my sisters got adopted we went out to Romania. I was about seven years old when I saw my biological mother. I didn't realise she was my mother until I got told later on that day. My biological mother also had one of my sisters with her, and I also didn't realise that she was my sister till later.

My sisters were I believe nine and ten when they got adopted; I was just approaching up to 12. They united the family when they were six and seven.

I do have a vivid memory of visiting Romania, I would never forget it. I remember wearing the most disgusting dress you could ever find in the drawer.

I remember the children and the orphanage where my sisters were. It was very traumatic because I realised the children spent 23 hours in a cot, drugged up to "keep them quiet", forced to sit on potties, forced to eat whatever they were given such as gruel, one meal a day. Children getting washed in cold water, I even watched carers shaving the children's hair off so they didn't get nits whether they were girl or boy. I remember saying to the carers, 'Don't shave my sister's hair off please'. I also remember watching the carers throwing the children into their cot. There was no affection or love between the carers and the children.

Some of the children had disabilities physically and most of them were mentally damaged. Also I remember when walking into my sisters' orphanage the other orphans would dart up to you, trying to seize onto you for attention, love and seeking for a mother.

But the worse and the most traumatic thing is I remember seeing my youngest sister screaming continuously in her cot. I felt helpless, hurt and remorseful for her.

We went to my sisters' orphanage quite a few times to see the girls. This is when my adoptive parents went on national TV and so there was some filming of my sisters, my adoptive parents and I in Romania. I never really comprehended why we went on TV.

But when I first saw my sisters I didn't know who they were let alone that they were my sisters. When I found out that they were I was eager because I would have "somebody to play with".

We were probably in Romania for at least two weeks; we went to Romania more than once. Suddenly we were flying off to go to Romania very early in the morning.

I liked Romania, it felt like home because at that time I knew this is where I belonged, and also the people in Romania were very different to the English people. They all spoke to each other and also I treasured how the women dressed – the Gypsies, dresses and scarves on their heads.

There were horses and carts which they used to farm the fields for fruit and vegetables, and everything was done by hand. In my eyes I thought it was a beautiful country.

My adoptive parents, sisters and I went back out to Romania when I was 14. That's when I met the full biological family; there was a lot of emotion, feeling angry, upset and confused when we went into their home. They couldn't speak English and I couldn't speak Hungarian which was the most frustrating part of it, yet it was lovely at the same time.

I remember when my two sisters, adoptive parents and I were walking up the wooden stairs, I was in front and my eldest sister stood at the door. I looked at her and I just broke down into tears and then she welcomed us and there I saw my other younger sister and my two younger brothers and my biological father, then about 20 minutes later my biological mother came in and hugged me. I wasn't really sure how I felt; I had different feelings spiralling around and angry thoughts building in my head.

Then my younger sister came in after school. Even though I don't really know her I feel I'm closer to her than anybody else in the biological family.

My adoptive parents left me and my two sisters with the biological parents. They went and did their own thing and my two sisters and I were left with the family for the whole day. When my adoptive parents left my younger sister whom I am closest to played some Gypsy music and taught me how to dance, also my biological mother would teach me words in Hungarian and I taught my little brother how to count in English.

But the way we would communicate is by drawing pictures and using sign language. It was hard and frustrating, but that was the only way to communicate with each other.

Later on in the day my biological mother took me to my biological father's work place and left my eldest sister to look after the younger siblings. My brother came with us; my biological father's work was as a road sweeper. When we got there my biological mother talked to her friends and I just played with my little brother; I thought that was lovely.

We then walked home on the road for some strange reason, and my biological mother started peeling the vegetables and cooked them by adding water and milk and some other strange stuff with it and she cooked pasta with it as well. She then served it up and placed a bowl of it in front of me and I didn't eat it because it looked too different, and I didn't feel the appetite for it; but I was hungry by the end of the day.

But when I left I felt annoyed about being left in an orphanage and never really got the answers from my biological mother. In my eyes they seemed to be a content family.

I wouldn't choose to see them again because they are not my family in my eyes and I don't know them, can't speak their language and it would be an absolute waste of time in seeing them again in my point of view.

I even have stopped the letter contact since last year; I was saying the same thing every year and it seemed meaningless and the hassle in getting translated and to be sincere, it's an absolute waste of time.

I used to get letters back from my biological mother, but since I left home I have only received one or two letters from her, but now I don't receive anything.

It taught me a lesson when I was in Romania: to stop taking things for granted, wanting more and more; stop reflect on other people who haven't got what you've got; appreciating what you've been given. They made the most of what they've got, which is nothing. But they are always content in their own way, which is incredible.

My trip to my orphanage (Social Welfare Institute)

Heather (Nan Ziyuan) Macrae (age 11)

My family and I have gone back to China almost every year since I was adopted in 1998. When we go there we see friends, visit playparks, go sightseeing and visit my Social Welfare Institute. When we go to the Social Welfare Institute, we give gifts from us and others from all over the world and talk to Ms Dao and the people who work there. This year, when we visited, I realised that I had changed a huge amount since we were last there, in 2007.

This year when we visited, my family was very eager to meet the girl who Mummy is sponsoring. She is a baby and she is called Zhao Yunshan.

Before we went to the Social Welfare Institute, we met up with our friend Michelle in our hotel room. Michelle is Chinese, and is an editor on a Chinese newspaper. She can speak English and Chinese fluently. Michelle was going to help us by translating what the Chinese nannies at the Social Welfare Institute were saying.

When we arrived we were warmly greeted by Ms Dao who is in charge of the children. Mummy handed me our donation 'for all the kids left behind' so that I could hand it over to the Social Welfare Institute, and they took me off to have it receipted. We also had lots of dress-up clothes and stickers and building bricks to give to the school classes – for special need kids – held in the orphanage. I made that donation, too, and had my photo taken with the official lady who helps run the scheme (Half the Sky).

When I was there, I felt that I knew my way around the first two floors just as well as I know my way around my own house, because we had been there so many times since I was adopted. We talked quite a lot with Ms Dao, and then we got to go and see Zhao Yunshan. When Mum and Dad approached her she cried. Ms Dao told us that she had got quite attached to her nanny and that she cried if anyone else tried to hold her.

After we had given them all our presents and had a look at all of the babies in the room a lady came in. She was wearing a blue apron/overall, had black curly hair and two crooked teeth. I thought I recognised her. She asked Ms Dao what my name was and when she found out that it was me, she squeezed me towards her and hugged me. It turned out that she was my nanny when I was a baby at the Social Welfare Institute. I was quite uncomfortable when she did the squeezy hugs on me, because she felt like a stranger to me. But I couldn't just tell her to get off me, because it would be rude. So I just let her do it. She told me and everyone in the room that she had been my nanny and that I used to be very naughty and climbed out my cot and spat my food out at mealtimes. She also told me where my cot had been when I was little. My mum and dad let me decide when I wanted to come back to them for a hug and protection! I felt quite funny about needing to get back to my mum, because I wanted to hear from my nanny, but she sort of made me feel squashed.

We were allowed to look at the babies! But when we were looking at the babies in the dull uninteresting room, I got angry. I wanted to say to the nannies that they weren't looking after the babies properly, because they were just propping the babies' bottles on the blankets so the babies had to do all the work. They didn't even hold the bottles to help the babies drink their milk. They weren't attending to the babies who were crying, or were upset, or making sure that the babies kept their heads out of the blankets so that they didn't run out of air. Also the nannies had the toddlers who were a little bit active tied to their cots. I thought that this was cruel and it made me feel helpless because I don't work there and I can't tell the nannies what to do.

After a few hours it was time to go. So we said our goodbyes (it takes an awful long time to say goodbye properly in China!) and flagged down a taxi, and went back to our hotel. As soon as possible after noodles for lunch (Mummy microwaved them in our room) we went to the playpark. I always need to run and swing and climb after visiting my orphanage; it helps me clear my thoughts. My sister Zoe and I went on LOADS of rides and it was great fun.

I think, right now, I am glad we met my nanny but I still am very unsure of her. I don't know if I like her or not because I don't know her very well and she is still a stranger to me now that I am me and not the me that was in the institute. I have memories of her being really rough with me and pinching me when she looked after me when I was a little kid in the Social Welfare Institute. She sometimes didn't care for me gently when I was small.

I guess this makes me feel scared every time somebody doesn't like me.

All about me

Veronica Whitehead (age 10)

My name is Veronica. I was adopted in Guatemala. It feels like I am different to my friends because sometimes people stare at me and ask questions. But it is really great having friends just like me who are also adopted from Guatemala and other countries – because I feel like I am not the only one.

When we first got to Guatemala I felt happy I was there and I could see what it was like and I felt at home in Guatemala. I had been so looking forward to it and it was kind of like I expected it to be.

We first went to the hotel where I first met my parents when I was a baby. I had heard lots of stories about it and had seen videos. It felt nice to be there. My mum and dad had talked to me about the fantastic breakfasts – and they were right.

While we were in Guatemala we studied Spanish in the mornings – and I wanted to stay there all day like at school in England. I played games in Spanish and got to have my teacher all to myself and I had a special classroom up on a hill – unlike the rest of my family who just got a small compartment each. My brother and I went to *Pollo Campero* (Guatemala's own fast-food chain of chicken restaurants) – which is really nice.

We went with the school to a co-operative and we bought a beautiful *huipil* and *cortes* for me – traditional Guatemalan dress. They explained the meaning of the colours in Guatemalan culture (for example, green is the colour of hope; red represents the east where the sun rises, the origin of civilization and life; black represents the decline of the day, the end of life and death). I was shown how to grind coffee on a traditional flat mortar (*metate y mano*) and how to make tortillas – but the fire on which they were cooked was horribly smoky. You couldn't really see and I coughed a lot.

We went to visit one of the projects we help to support. I felt upset that the families don't have a home like we do here but things had been improved so much – they now have clean water and gardens and a school and stoves to stop the smoke hurting everyone, especially the children and babies.

We went to see my foster mother and her new family. I really enjoyed seeing her and she made a fuss of me. The house was full of people and children – my foster mother lives with her mother and brother and sisters and their children! They still look after children, some of whom are going to be adopted and some just live there.

I was really upset because I didn't get to see my birth mother and family. I really miss them and wish I could meet them and see if I have brothers and sisters and see if they look like me and like the same things as me and are as bendy as me! But I did get to see my brother's birth family and his brothers and they were really nice.

I would like to go back to Guatemala soon and try again to see if I can meet my birth mother and family.

The colours in me by Veronica Whitehead (age 10)

The most beautiful country in the world

Ossie Whitehead (age 11)

In summer 2006 when I was nine my family and I went back to Guatemala where I was born. It felt a bit weird because I can't remember being there when I was young – I was nearly three when I left.

Of course I looked the same as everybody else – which felt like I belong there. I had been studying Spanish for years – and we always have a Spanish-speaking student in our home – but it was still really hard understanding people, especially since they expected me to understand them. We studied Spanish some more – it was fun. My teacher joked with me when we played games and took me and my sister out for trips – the best one was to *Pollo Campero*, Guatemala's own fast-food chain, which should be more famous than McDonalds.

I hated one thing – there were too many insects – especially spiders which scare me so badly.

We did lots of shopping – bought Guatemalan football kit for me and my sister and some of my friends who were also born in Guatemala. We visited some amazing Mayan ruins. We saw huge gigantic lizards and iguanas, bright coloured parrots and fascinating leaf cutter ants marching in a long line coming down from the trees. The best bit was the ball court, where they said that the losing team would be sacrificed to the Gods. Players were not allowed to use hands and feet to get the ball through the ring high up on the wall. The carvings and Mayan symbols were kind of cool – especially the rows of skulls!

We went on a couple of other trips to see a project our family support and a little boy who we sponsor. We had to sit in the new school which we had helped to have built while the village leaders made speeches – it was really boring (only Dad really understood what they were saying). But then we went round the village and had a chance to see how people lived – after things had been made better. They had water and toilets and kitchen gardens – I got a brilliant carrot to eat. It made me really think how it must have been hard before all these changes. Later I saw a hummingbird – it was beautifully coloured like a rainbow.

We also went to see the boy we sponsor. His family made us really welcome with some incredibly loud fireworks. They scared me at first because I did not know what was happening, then I thought it was awesome. Thousands of bangs and thick clouds of smoke! They had made a poster to say welcome and thank you. They gave us a lunch with nice sandwiches and weird fizzy drinks.

On both trips we (my sister and I) were allowed to travel in the back of pick-up trucks which we would never be allowed to do here which was so exciting!

I felt quite proud of helping people in Guatemala.

I felt happy that I was going to meet my brothers and my birth mummy again. They live miles away from where we were staying so we had to get up incredibly early – I was so tired and it was such a long way. Luckily we stopped for breakfast after a few hours.

We stopped once at a place where a bank beside the road had collapsed and we collected loads of obsidian which the Maya used as knives and weapons. Then we got to the town near where I was born and we went to the central park to meet my birth family. The park was crowded – it was Sunday – with loads of families out walking. We waited and waited and then finally my birth family came. I recognised my birth mummy straight away from the photos I keep in my bedroom. But there was a panic. Eduardo, one of my brothers, was missing. I was terrified! All the grown-ups set off in groups to find him and a few moments later it was all OK – he had been found. It was not the start I had expected but it stopped us all standing around looking awkward!

It felt warm when I hugged M my birth mother. I was surprised at how many of the family came to see me: all three of my brothers, my grandmother and grandfather, and half a dozen assorted uncles, aunts, cousins, etc. M was so brave, she looked sad and happy and she was so nice to me and my sister. Mum and Dad had been worried that everything was going to be OK and there was lots of happy crying going on. We all set off for *Pollo Campero* where we sat down to talk. Everyone was talking at the same time and it was so noisy. My sister and I played with my brothers, cousins and aunts and uncles (some of whom are younger than me!) We tried to find out some more information on how the family are doing. Afterwards we went somewhere a bit more private to give the family some presents – my brothers all got England football shirts and sleeping bags – and we gave them loads of photos of me and my sister. I felt sad when it was time to say goodbye. I got lots of hugs and kisses from M and my brothers and we waved until they walked out of sight.

It was a long drive back to where we were staying.

I really look forward to going back to Guatemala soon and seeing M and my brothers again.

My journey back to Thailand

Joshua (age 12)

I want to tell you about my journey back to my birth place, Thailand, and how I felt about it. My mum and dad have taken me back a few times but the last visit in the summer of 2006 was the most important visit for me.

The Thai government organises every three years a Nativeland Visit which is a week-long visit for adopted Thai kids and their families back to their homeland. Can you imagine, we were 650 people from 15 countries? There were over 280 children and their parents. In Bangkok, the capital of Thailand, we all stayed in the very nice Dusit Thani Hotel. I felt surprised that there were so many Thai children adopted all around the world. Sometimes in London I feel like I am the only Thai adopted child although we often meet up with lots of adopted Thai kids. It was such a good experience and I felt happy to be there.

In Thailand we did many fun things like meeting up with a Thai princess. There was also a big welcome ceremony with lots of children dancing dressed in very colourful clothes, traditional Thai music and lovely Thai food. I almost fell asleep because I had jetlag. It was our first day and I could not sleep very much. All the children had to walk on to a stage where five people were sitting and tying wristbands on us. This means they were welcoming us into Thai culture.

Wherever we travelled, we travelled in 15 buses with police escort. I remember it was so hot on the way to the meeting with the princess. We did not have to stop at the traffic lights because we were travelling as VIPs (very important people). It made me feel special and that the government welcomed us and cared a lot about us.

The day after, we went to the Babies Home where I had lived for the first two years of my life. My mum and dad had picked me up from there ten years ago. I felt quite awkward because all the carers were fussing over me. They still remembered me and I remembered my time there. That day didn't feel very good for me. I had so many bad and embarrassed feelings. I felt happy that I was me and that my adoption had turned out so well and that these people cared so much for me but I felt ashamed that I ever lived in a children's home. They really made us feel very welcome with music, they made a film for us, they gave us lovely food and they had taken the trouble to put up photographs of us when we were babies. Mummy cried again.

After a few days when I felt I was ready we went to visit my birth father. I don't want to give his real name, so I will call him Thon. Two years earlier I wanted to know what my birth parents look like and my parents asked a private investigator in Thailand to trace them. My birth father was very happy and wanted to meet me but my birth mother didn't feel ready.

My birth father lives in the northeast, a poor part of Thailand, and when the government took us there, we left and went on our own to meet my birth father. A friend's mum had found a very good driver and translator. We drove for four hours and met my birth father in a small town.

I didn't know what it was going to be like and I felt quite anxious. I had so many questions. My most important question I wanted to ask was why did you leave me? When I first met him I felt a bit angry in my heart that he had left me. But I thought that he had a good reason because he is a good person. Before I went I hoped that my questions would be answered and that I could also meet my birth mother. When I met my birth father, I felt so nervous and I couldn't ask the question but my mum asked and I got the answer. That made me happy. But I was annoyed that my birth mother was not ready to meet me. I think she should have.

When I first saw him, I felt a bit nervous and I didn't know what to say. My daddy asked the first question. He said to Thon: 'Do you think he looks like you?'

Thon said, 'No, he looks just like his birth mother.'

I could see that he didn't look like me but I felt that he was my beginning and my past. And then I looked at my mum and dad and felt they were my future. I was looking for similarities but I couldn't find any. If I had just met him without knowing who he was, I would have never thought so.

My mum had made a photo album for my birth father to show him how I had grown up and what my life was like in England. He was very happy to see all the photos and we talked about my life. He wanted to know whether I was doing well at school and whether I am a good eater. He was surprised to hear that I had many Thai friends and that we go to a Thai temple to celebrate the Thai festivals.

I felt awkward because he was my past but in a way I didn't know him at all. As we were talking to him it felt as if I was uncovering my past.

I asked my dad whether he could take a photo of myself and my birth father; I thought he is my beginning and just in case I never see him again, I wanted to remember him. Then I took photos of my mum and dad and my birth father because for me it felt like here were my two families united and happy. It made me feel at peace. I felt happy because my two families were together.

I started feeling more relaxed and everyone was chatting and it felt a nice atmosphere. Mummy then asked me whether I was ready to go to the village to meet all the other relatives. I felt I could do it. We went by car and it only took five minutes to get to the village. I remembered the house from the photographs the private investigator had sent us. My grandfather was there. He took my hands and looked at me and said, 'You don't look like a Thai boy.'

I said, 'Maybe I have been living in England for too long,' and we all laughed.

Then lots of people started coming to the house – aunts, cousins, grandmother and neighbours. They all wanted to see me and I felt like a celebrity. And I felt happy and I felt at peace. Everyone was asking questions about me and my life in England. Then my birth father, grandfather and grandmother started a ceremony – they knelt in front of us and tied wristbands on me and Mummy and Daddy. I felt so welcomed and it also felt nice for me because they were welcoming Mummy and Daddy too.

Thai village

I sometimes felt if I lived there, I would have been part of this community and then I would have known my birth father much better. But then I wouldn't be with my mum and dad and that would make me very sad. I know we will visit my birth father again and Mummy writes to him and he writes to us.

We went back the next day and played some football outside the house. And my birth father told me that I have a stepsister who is three years younger than me. It made me feel happy to know that I have a stepsister but I was sad that I couldn't meet her. I hope one day I will meet her. I felt sad when we left because it felt like I was leaving something behind.

After I had met my birth father it made me feel like I was free of a burden that I had carried for a long time. The visit lit up my life and made me hopeful for the future. I feel I have got some better understanding of my life and my past and I feel more confident about my future.

All about me

Ruth Ling Dooley (age 6)

I would really like to go back to China some day. I would like to see the Geat Wall. My Chinese name is Xu Rui Ling. I was born in the year of the Dragon. I love my mam and dad.

SECTION 6

Messages

Advice for young people waiting to be adopted

Mack (age 12), Victoria (age 13), Chelsey (age 12) and Smurfy (age 15)

Being adopted is cool so don't be scared.

Mack

I would tell them it's not as bad as it seems. I wish someone told me that it is not as bad as it seems.

Victoria

Go ahead and have a nice time with your new family!

Chelsey

No need to worry!! Talk to the new family and get to know them. If there's any problems talk to someone, e.g. a social worker. If you're scared, talk to someone.

Smurfy

Dear all adopted children

Michael (age 13)

All I can say is your life is no different to anyone else's. Live your life as you would expect any other person would live theirs. Make lots of friends, join in lots of clubs and try to make the best of your life. Be extra kind to your adoptive parents because remember they are the ones that brought you into their lives and they deserve credit for that.

As for the adoptive parents, my advice is to try not to mention too much about them being adopted; just celebrate the day they were adopted each year and remind them that that was the day when they became a part of your family. Remember if the children are five or over you will need to be extra kind because they may not be used to being away from their birth parents or foster carers.

As for teachers, some details of adopted children's lives are unavailable so if you are going to ask them, try to do it diplomatically. As for parents' evening, try to remember that the child's parents are their adoptive parents so they can give more advice to you if you need it.

For social workers, try to note down important things because they will help you get to know the adopted child. Things like names of birth parents, or where they grew up, how old they were when they were adopted or if they are comfortable with their adoptive parents. If they don't feel comfortable answering these questions try asking them a different question.

For me I can sum up being adopted in a sentence: 'I just feel like I'm a normal kid.'

Young people's top tips

Young people from Adoption Support, Coram Family and
St. Francis Children's Society

In March 2006, adopted young people from the above organisations came together for a weekend conference in Northampton called 'Adopted Young People: Our messages'. Twenty-three young people aged 15–21 years took part. The conference aimed to provide a platform for young people to have an input in plans and possible decisions that are made for adopted children and young people at a local, even national, level – in essence, for adopted young people to tell the "powers that be" what they want. The themes explored were education, contact and identity.

• We want to know more about our backgrounds.

• Everyone involved needs to be open and honest.

• Some of us feel we are ready to meet our birth family before we are 18.

• Tell us where we can go for help.

• We think it would be good to have a helpline and support from an older adopted young person.

• Sometimes we feel our family and people at school don't understand us or listen to us.

• Support adopters to talk to their adopted child . . . it doesn't always get talked about.

• We would like to know more about our adoptive parents before we go to live with them.

• Teachers and pupils need to be taught more about adoption.
  – If you can't rely on a teacher who can you rely on?

• Involve us in training people to become adopters.
  – We think we'd be good at it!

Untitled

Luke Howard (age 10)

I would like to say to other adopted children that no one should be grateful to be adopted, but see that we all needed to be and our new families are grateful to have us.

Parents can help us by loving who we are – maybe they imagined a different kind of child but if they try and shape us too roughly to become someone else we will probably break!

I have no idea of social workers because I was too young, but they should never stop anyone being a parent because they are different from their ideas of what an adopter should be. I have adoptive parents who have 14 other children; they are a different colour and still we are the same family.

Teachers do not understand that we are adopted kids, but we do not always have our birth families' problems. We had problem families – we are not problem children.

I am lucky. I hate people being sad for me.

Life

Fiona Higham (at age 18)

Life is made up of some pretty strange stuff
Who knows what tomorrow brings,
Happiness, sadness
Or maybe just a plain boring day.

Maybe something wonderful might happen
Who knows what tomorrow brings
Maybe something tragic might happen

We should all live life as if today is our last day
Who knows what tomorrow brings
We can't regret what we do
Or regret what we don't do

We have to be ourselves
And get what we want from life
Because life is what we make it
It could be good it could be bad
Who knows what tomorrow brings

We don't choose what happens in the world
But if we do get up in the morning
Make sure you have done everything today
Not just anything
Because life is precious

One minute it's there
The next minute it could be gone
So tell that person you love them
Tell that person you are sorry
Make friends with that enemy
See yourself in a new light
Before you see the light of heaven.

Live every day as if it's your last
Be proud when you go to sleep at night

Smile to yourself before you go to bed
Look up and see who gave you this life

Realise you don't decide when it's taken from you
No one can give you a more beautiful gift than the gift of life
Life is the most sacred possession you own
You can control it

Three messages

Terezia Dziubak (age 20)

The message I would have for other adopted people is know who you really are and know who your biological parents are when you're ready.

A message I would have for parents, who are adopted themselves, give your child as much love and attention that you would have wanted when you were a child; they don't need the latest toy out, and the child wants YOU!!!

The message I would have for social services is, through my own experience, only allow people who want to adopt, to only adopt one child and also ensure they would be able to cope and be able to reach the child's needs.

Huggles and snuggles

Ronan (age 4)

Have lots of love,
kisses and huggles,
and snuggles and cuddly
On the sofa

from

RONAN

I send you a rainbow

Adopted Ukraine 2004

My message to other adopted children

Anna Maria Silvia (age 7)

It's excellent being adopted because you get to know a different country.

It is also sad because you miss the rest of your family. It's OK to be sad and talk about it a lot.

Talking about it helps you to remember your special birth family.

You can have space in your hearts for all your families.

Another thing I do to remember my faraway family is to light special candles on my birthday.

And do take care of your forever family.

My message to social workers

Marcus Wootton-Kahn (age 20)

Don't prevent someone who wants to be adopted from getting adopted.

Listen to what the child is saying.

Don't tell them that adoption is the same as fostering!

And remember, I may have a learning disability but I am smart!

Some advice

Ruby (age 7)

When I got adopted I felt comfortable. My sisters helped me, and they and my mummy and daddy kept on being nice to me and helped me get used to them. I think adopted children should get information from the orphanage and go and see it if they can, which made me feel very happy because it helped me remember the past when I was young in the orphanage.

Tips for adoptive parents

Christina Cole-Wilson (age 18)

Welcome them into the house and into your world and your family.

Treat them nicely, don't abuse them.

For children, parents and social workers

Sola (age 12)

For adopted children

It seems really weird to think you are going to be calling someone else mum and dad and you may be unsure about the whole idea. I was. But it all turns out at least ten times better than you expected it to. I found that because you are chosen they are prepared and have most things ready for you and unlike some of your friends at school who were born by accident, they wanted you and they picked you.

For parents

You would make your new child feel more happy and secure if you let them settle at their own pace. Make sure that the child has some of their old belongings that comfort them around them so they feel that they are not completely in a new atmosphere. Don't expect to be called mummy straight away and at bedtimes just sit them down, give them a hug and make them feel nice and explain to them how they shouldn't feel pressured into anything they don't want to such as calling you mummy. Tell all the other relatives not to be constantly kissing and hugging the child as it makes them feel uncomfortable. Let them get to know them first.

For parents

If you adopt a child with brothers and sisters it's really vital you let them keep in touch and meet up as it's an important part of them and their lives. My sister went to a family that wiped out her past and don't let her see me and it tears me apart.

For social workers

You should make sure when visiting foster homes to look beyond what is on the surface. For example, my foster carer was abusive to me. I was too young and too scared to tell the social worker who was the only other person I ever saw. All the signs were there if only the social worker had looked – there were lots of injuries but she just believed the reasons the foster carer gave her.

A message for therapists

Julia (age 15)

I am writing only about my experiences and what has happened to me in the past. My therapist I have had for a while isn't specialised in adoption but helps me with the issues surrounding that as well as other issues. I also have a new therapist who specialises in adoption.

Being in therapy is a terrifying experience at times and can be very daunting. The most important thing to do if an adopted child opens up to you is to try and acknowledge their feelings and realise that, however irrational or rational the feelings or thoughts may seem that the child is talking about, they are very real and scary for the child. Reassure the child that it could not possibly be their fault no matter what happened and that no matter how hard their past has been remind them that the future may hold something brighter and it is worth fighting for.

My current therapist is always so sweet and although she cannot understand exactly how I feel she listens to me. When I feel sad she says that's OK and when I say I am angry she says that is OK. What I feel is never wrong. She helps me as to how to deal with those feelings. She always knows when I am upset and she helps me just by being smiley and happy. I think it is crucial for a therapist to be happy and smiley and make the person feel that they are worth something as it may feel difficult for the child to feel that they are worth anything and that what they think or feel is worth anything at all.

My new therapist is helping me sort out my feelings and past through various art therapy methods such as using a sand tray and drawing. I find this a lot more difficult to deal with but I feel this may be a better way to work with younger adopted children than talking may be. I find talking a lot easier as when I play with the sand or draw I feel like a small child which makes me feel more vulnerable and things seem a lot bigger. Any type of therapy takes some getting used to so it's good to be patient and kind and if the child doesn't open up to you or do the things you ask the first time, give them time.

My current therapist who I have seen for a while has changed my life. You will be a big part of the adoptee's life you are working with. My therapist has always been so lovely and helped me to express things which I found difficult. I'm sure my new therapist will be nice and helpful too but it takes time to trust new people. Time is important and being smiley and welcoming and validating the adoptee's feelings is crucial.

If all people were like my therapist, J, the world would be an amazing place.

For other adoptees

Heather (Nan Ziyuan) Macrae (age 11)

See the past as the past and reach for the future. Talk with your mum and dad about birth parents sometimes, but don't dwell on it. They (birth parents) aren't here and you have a whole life to live, so get on with it. Enjoy going back to your birth country for its own sake and maybe for the future, but not to find the past.

All you adopted people!

Amy (age 17)

My message to all you adopted people out there!

Believe: believe in yourself, believe you can make it, believe in those around you, believe that you are loved, and believe that YOUR life has probably changed for the better!

For everyone

Jessica (age 10)

It's hard work but it's worth it – and that's for everyone.

For parents and children:

At the end of the day it's great to have a family.

A note to adopted children

Julia (age 15)

Being adopted isn't easy at any stage in your life. Although you get older being an adopted adolescent is just as hard as it brings up more thoughts of belonging. Some days it doesn't bother me but other days it is all I can think of.

Being adopted makes you wonder where you came from. Thoughts like 'Was I loved? Does anyone actually care? Will anyone love me? What did I do wrong?' are all natural feelings for an adopted child but remember, it wasn't your fault and adoption is nothing to feel ashamed about. All these things are just feelings, they will go away.

The trick is to try and hang in there, as hard as that may seem. Remember that people do care about you and adoption is never the child's fault.

A passage that helps me is: 'To the world you may be one person but to one person you may be the world.'

About the contributors

Alison was born in the south of England in 1994 and is of white British parentage. She went into care when she was six years old and lived with one set of foster carers before moving to her adoptive family when she was seven. Alison enjoys reading, singing and being a "drama queen"! She is happiest when she is hanging out with friends. Alison hopes to work with languages or be an actress. She lives in northern England with her mum and dad and does not have any contact with her birth family.

Anita Nitiluk Hennessey was born in 1993 in Bangkok, Thailand. She lived in an orphanage for four years before being adopted by Mortimer and Eilish Hennessy in the Republic of Ireland. Anita also has a brother, Eimhin (Evin), and two sisters, Patricia (Trisha) and Muire. She likes the music of Westlife and Rihanna and playing football. She is happiest when she is going to the cinema with her friends or playing with her pet dog Buddy. Anita hopes to become a model when she is older.

AB was born in 1996 in Hunan province in China. She lived in a social welfare institute for the first 15 months of her life before moving to England when she was adopted. Her adoptive family is made up of mum and dad, an older brother and sister and a younger sister who is also adopted from China. AB would love to meet her birth family, though she knows this is unlikely. She has visited China once and the family is planning a return trip in 2009. AB loves being with her friends, swimming and riding her bike. She hates exams and homework.

Anna Maria Silvia was born in Guatemala seven years ago. When she was in the children's home they used to call her Patricia or Patti. Her mummy Silvia gave her the names Silvia and Patricia, and her mummy Judy gave her the other names. She lives in Reading, which is not as sunny as Guatemala. She visited Guatemala when she was four and hopes to go back in 2009. Anna is a fan of *High School Musical* films and Shakespeare. She also likes going to the theatre, visiting

her grandma and grandpa by the sea, telling funny jokes and dancing. She has five sisters and one brother, who live in Guatemala, Canada and Heaven. Anna really likes being with her twin sisters in Canada, who are a year older than her but the same height. When she grows up she wants to be a pop star and an opera singer. She wishes that she could see mummy Silvia again and that there were no wars in the world.

Anthony, now 14, is white English. He had a number of moves in and out of care before being removed permanently when he was three. He then had one placement before he and his older brother James were adopted at the ages of five (Anthony) and seven (James). Both boys are mad on sport. Anthony has represented his mainstream school at athletics and cricket, is in three sports teams (cricket, football and athletics) and volunteers with a swimming club for younger children with disabilities. He also enjoys going to the theatre and meeting up with friends. The family had a campervan for six years and toured Europe, and last year James and Anthony and their parents went to Nepal for two weeks to help teach visually impaired football and cricket to blind children. Anthony wants to be a sports development officer or PE teacher. He lives in London.

Amy was born in Solihull and is of white British heritage. She was placed for adoption at the age of five and has had indirect contact with her birth mother and direct contact with her birth father. Amy also has indirect contact with her siblings placed for adoption in separate families. She adjusted well to her adoptive family and it was not until she hit adolescence that she started to experience difficulties with her adoption identity. With the help of friends, family and adoption support agencies she has worked very hard to come to terms with these issues that all adopted young people face. She is now very settled and has recently become engaged to be married. Amy has experienced hidden minefields in her adoption journey and hopes that her poem 'Lucky?!' helps others to appreciate that the journey can be hard but support can get you through it.

Amy Leigh was born in 1999 in Changning, China, shortly before the millennium. She is of Chinese parentage. When she was newborn Amy was left by her birth family outside the police station and taken from there to the local orphanage where she stayed for 14 months before joining her adoptive family. Her birth family is unknown. Amy lives with her mum and dad and older sister Victoria in London. She is happiest when dressing up and eating Italian food! Her favourite subject is maths and she says she wants to be a banker.

Ayesha was born in 1996 of white Scottish and Asian British parentage. She lived with foster carers from birth until she was seven months old when she joined her adoptive family. Ayesha does not have any contact with her birth family. She enjoys swimming, climbing and lots of other sports. She is happiest when she is with her best friend Reece and on holiday with her family. Her hopes for the future are to achieve a gold medal at the Olympic Games for swimming and running. Ayesha lives in England with her younger adoptive brother and sister and kitten Honey.

Chantelle was born in 1994 in Northampton. She went into care when she was five years old and lived with three sets of foster carers before moving to her adoptive family when she was six. She lives with her mum and dad and two older brothers. Chantelle has contact with a birth brother and sister. She enjoys horse riding and karate and hopes to work with children when she is older.

Charlene Stagles was born in 1983 in Harlow and is of "Gypsy" parentage. She joined her adoptive family in London when she was four years old. Charlene found it very difficult that she had not been in the same tummy as her sister, Ellen, and brother, Tommy, who are not adopted. Charlene is the youngest and has cerebral palsy and learning difficulties.

The family moved to Wales when Charlene was eight. Then, when she was 14, they spent three years in Ebolowa, Cameroon. Charlene always went to mainstream school and attended the English-speaking mainstream school in Ebolowa. She spoke about her adoption with the refugee children in her class because they, too, did not know where their birth parents were. She does not have any contact with her birth family.

Charlene loves traveling and went to Mombassa in Kenya for a conference on community-based rehabilitation and visited her friend Hanta in Madagascar. She also visits her brother Tom who lives in Holland. She is very independent. At the moment, she lives in supported housing not far from her special friend, Mark. Her sister Ellen lives nearby.

Chelsey is 12 and white British. She joined her adoptive family around four years ago, along with her sister, and has some contact with her siblings. Chelsey enjoys spending time with friends, watching movies, computer and playing football. She lives in England.

Christina Cole-Wilson was born in 1989 in England and is of African-Caribbean descent. She was fostered as a baby and placed for adoption at two years and one month. Christina is in the third year of sixth form and lives in London with her adoptive mother and older brother. Her favourite hobbies are singing, drama, going away and dance. She is happiest when going out for a meal. Christina does not currently have contact with her birth family but would like to do so.

Claire was born in 1995 in the south of England and is of white British parentage. She went into care when she was five years old and lived with one set of foster carers before moving to her adoptive family when she was six. Claire lives with her mum and dad in the north of England. She does not have any contact with her birth family. She enjoys sports and reading and is happiest when with friends and family. Claire hopes to be a scientist.

Conor Howard is eight years old and of mixed heritage. He was born withdrawing from drugs and adopted after being physically abused in foster care as he recovered from being a drug-addicted baby. Conor is of unknown ethnicity and has no contact with his birth family. As a result of his injuries, he is learning and behaviourally damaged and recognised as disabled. Conor loves the computer and enjoys playing rugby. He lives in England.

Conor Henry was born in Thailand in October 2001. He was adopted at the age of 21 months and now lives in Ireland with his mum and dad and younger sister, also adopted from Thailand. Conor enjoys swimming, reading, drawing and music and is very athletic. He has a great interest in sea life, especially jellyfish, and when the family visited Thailand in 2007, he very much enjoyed his trip to Siam Ocean World Aquarium, Bangkok. Conor hopes to become a pilot and loves planning adventures with his favourite toy, Pilchard.

Daniel was born in 1998 in the London area. His birth parents are of white British and dual heritage (African and white British) background. He went into care when he was four months old and lived with one foster carer before moving to his adoptive family at 16 months. Daniel lives with his mum and dad, two sisters and a brother. He has annual contact with his birth brothers and two-way letterbox contact with his birth mother. He enjoys football and performing arts and is happiest on the beach making sandcastles.

David Joel Helliwell was born on 6 January 1988 in Luton, of Pakistani and English parentage. He was adopted at the age of one as his birth mum had been left by his birth father. He grew up in Northamptonshire with his parents Christine and Keith and his adopted sister Rachel. He has known he was adopted for as long as he can remember. In early November 2007, he received a call from an adoption agency telling him that he has a younger half-sister, aged 16, whom he never knew existed. David enjoys music and is a self-taught drummer. He also likes to keep active and is a keen mountain biker. He is currently living in Northamptonshire and is 19 years old.

Davina was born in southern England to white British birth parents. She is the middle child of three girls. Davina has lived with six sets of foster carers and in a total of ten homes due to different foster placements and moving around with her birth parents. She joined her adoptive family – mum, dad and birth sister Harriet – when she was almost six. Only two of her four grandparents remain, but she has lots of aunties, uncles and cousins. Davina has direct contact with her younger sister and and receives cards and vouchers from other birth family members for birthdays and Christmas. She loves meeting the sister she doesn't live with as well as being with her immediate and wider adoptive family. She lives in the Midlands.

Elizabeth was born in July 1990 in Romania. She was adopted from Romania at the age of seven weeks and has been living in the UK ever since. Since finishing school she has applied to study medicine at university and is currently working as a Physician's Assistant at her local hospital.

Ellie was born in Bulgaria in 2001 and lived there until she was adopted at two years of age. Ellie now lives in Northern Ireland with her mum, dad and little sister. She does not have contact with her birth family but has returned to Bulgaria on holiday. Ellie enjoys swimming and playing with her friends and cousins. She loves her dog Sam, a springer spaniel, and likes taking him for walks by the river.

Elliot was born in London in 1996 and is black British. He was two weeks old when he joined his adoptive family and two-and-a-half when his adoption order was finalised. Elliot lives in London with his mum who is also black British. He likes using the computer, going on day trips, rollercoasters and playing with model cars. Elliot would like to earn lots of money when he grows up.

Emily Cox was born on 28 April 1999 and adopted on 17 March 2000 in China. She lives with her mum Heather, dad Roger, sister Harriet and Wilma the cat. She loves Harry Potter, reading and making 'amazing origami'!

Eoin Andrei was born in 1999 in Birlad, Vaslui, Romania. He was in an orphanage until he was adopted three days before his first birthday. Eoin now lives in County Cork, Ireland, with his mam and dad and his younger brother who is adopted from Russia. He has not visited Romania since being adopted but says that he would love to go there some day. He does not have any contact with his birth family though he would like to meet  them one day. He enjoys sports very much, playing hurling, Gaelic football and soccer. Eoin hopes to some day meet a famous Liverpool soccer player.

Fiona Higham was born in Birmingham on 13 May 1983 to young white teenagers. She was badly affected by the rejection of her birth mother and the huge disruption she suffered during the first three years of her life stayed with her until she died at 19.

Fiona, three, and her younger sister Claire, aged two, were adopted together. Fiona had the voice of an angel and sang at every opportunity and would love to perform for others in school concerts, at Guide camp, on stage in talent shows . . . wherever she could. It made her so proud and happy. She was very creative both in her prose writing and poetry and she would always prefer to make birthday cards and Mother's Day cards than buy them. Words – written not spoken – were everything to her. She wrote down all her feelings, everything she couldn't get out from inside her head. She wrote pages and pages about how she felt about adoption and wanted others to understand what an adopted child feels but may not be able to talk about.

Although she was always in trouble at school for being disruptive, she actually loved the familiarity and security of school life. However, she decided to leave school at 16 and go to college to study midwifery but could not settle on any of the courses. Her past began to really haunt her. To numb her feelings she drank, moderately at first and then heavily. She ended up mixing with drug users and alcoholics and rejected all help from her parents, who refused to give up on her. Counsellors, clinics and every support network available tried to help but she wasn't ready to take it.

Sadly, on 23 June 2002, Fiona died from taking drugs at a house party. She had a chest infection and her respiratory system failed.

Francis Davies was born in London in 1990 and is white British. He joined his adoptive family when he was around eight-and-a-half. The court case was an interesting experience; it was over so fast, if he had have blinked he would have missed it! Francis is a drummer. He makes music, listens to music and goes to gigs. He also likes doing art – digital, 3D, 2D and traditional art (drawing, etc.) – and writes a lot of stories and poetry.

George was born in 1986 in Eastern Europe and adopted by his foster carer of three years at the age of 17. He lives in Wales.

Georgie was born in England in 1996. She was fostered with her younger sister when she was four-and-a-half and moved to her adoptive family with her sister when she was six. Georgie now lives outside the UK. Her younger brother was adopted by a different family and they are in touch. Georgie is creative and artistic, and loves cats and butterflies. She loves cuddling her cat and swimming. She is at her happiest when she is amongst all her cousins, playing.

Harriet Cox was born on 12 December 2001 and adopted on 23 September 2002 in China. She lives with her mum, dad, sister Emily and cat Wilma. Harriet loves dancing and adores her teddy Sophie!

Harriet was born in the south of England to white British birth parents. She is the eldest of three children and experienced numerous moves before joining her adoptive family at the age of six. Her family consists of her mum, dad and birth sister Davina. Harriet has direct contact with her youngest sister and letterbox contact with other birth family members. She enjoys seaside holidays and hopes to be a dog handler. Harriet is happiest when she is with her family.

Heather (Nan Ziyuan) Macrae was born in China in October 1996 and adopted in April 1998. She now lives in southern England with her younger sister (also adopted from China) and her Scottish parents. She is a keen artist and has for some years drawn most of her adoption work as "heart art". She loves all sport and is now playing competitively at secondary school. Heather loves family visits to China.

Henry is in his teens and lives with his adoptive family in the UK.

Holly Brooksbank was born in Mansfield in 1988. She was first in foster care at the age of one month to five months, then again until she was 14 months old. Holly went into care again for two-and-a-half years and spent four months with her birth mother before her final removal into care. She moved in with her adoptive family in 1994. Holly is a qualified hairdresser and lives in the Midlands. She enjoys being around animals and would love to work with them.

Jade was born in 1997 in Essex. She is of Irish, Pakistani and English parentage. She first went into care at 15 months and later aged three following the death of her mother. She lived with two sets of foster carers and with her birth father before joining her English adoptive mother at the age of seven. Jade enjoys swimming, scuba diving, playing with her friends and school – especially science lessons. She loves animals and has a dog named Toby and a hamster called Winner. She hopes to one day become a zoologist and work on a Safari Park in southern Africa. Jade lives in London.

James, now 16, is white English and has recently left school to start an apprenticeship. He experienced six moves in and out of care before being removed permanently when he was five. He then had three placements before he and his younger brother Anthony were placed for adoption at the ages of five and seven. James has always had a lot of contact with his older birth sister who remained in care and most holidays travels the 100 miles by train to go and stay with her and her boyfriend for a few days. He has two older brothers in his adoptive family, also adopted. He enjoys music, holidays, playing and watching football. He meets up with his friends most weekends to go out and has recently started a part-time job. James is also a very creative cook and enjoys cooking dinner for the family one night a week. He has been volunteering in a junior youth club and this summer (2008) is touring Barbados with his visually impaired cricket team. He wants to work in the construction industry and have enough money to get a car and to travel more. James lives in London.

Jane was born in 1990 in the northwest of England. She is of mixed British and Asian descent, including a quarter Pakistani. Jane went into care when she was a month old and joined her adoptive family when she was one. Her adoptive family comprises mum, dad and one older adopted sister. She does not have any contact with her birth family apart from a younger half-brother who is also adopted. Jane is at college studying animal care and lives in southwest England.

Jasmine was born in England in 1997 and is of mixed parentage. She went into care when she was a month old and lived with her foster parents before moving to her adoptive family at 15 months. Contact with Jasmine's siblings has proved to be very difficult and she is not in touch with her birth parents. Jasmine enjoys singing, dancing and music and is happiest when playing tag, or hide and seek. She hopes to become a teacher, singer, musician or doctor. Her mum thinks she would be great in some sort of caring capacity as she is a wonderfully caring person, especially with those who are less fortunate than herself.

Jason was born in 1998 in the West Midlands and, together with his younger sister, was adopted in 2002 at the age of four after only one short foster placement. The children have sporadic letterbox contact with their birth mother. Jason loves animals and science and has a really strong imagination. He especially enjoys games with dinosaurs and knights. Jason is a very caring, attentive and bright young man, who often takes an unusual view of situations that can make adults think differently. His parents are very proud of him.

Jeremy was born in 1995 and went into care with his three siblings when he was six years old. He was nine when he and his younger sister joined their adoptive family in the south of England. At that time, Jeremy could not read and could hardly write. He wrote 'Being adopted' without any help. Jeremy loves sport, especially cricket, tennis and athletics. He also plays rugby during winter. He is doing well at school, where his teachers talk fondly of him. Jeremy's parents are very proud of him.

Jess Peterson used to be known as Jessica Valen. She was born in 1991 in England and lives with her mum, dad and brother in Berkshire. Jess's birth father was English and her birth mother was half Caribbean. Jess's hobbies include riding and playing the piano.

Jessica was born in 1998 in the south of England and is of white British parentage. She went into care when she was two years old and lived with one set of foster carers before moving to her adoptive family when she was three. Jessica lives with her mum and dad. She does not have any contact her birth family. Jessica enjoys reading and hopes to be a writer. She lives in northern England and is happiest when she is with her family.

Jordan was born in Keighley, Yorkshire in August of 1990 of white parentage. He went into foster care at the age of four and had two foster families before moving to his adoptive parents when he was seven. He does not have any contact with his birth family. Jordan lives in southwest England and is currently at college doing a sports course. He has attended groups for adopted young people at CCS Adoption for the last 11 years. He mainly enjoys playing cricket, spending time with his parents and helping out at CCS to improve other young people's lives.

Josephine Chunrui Jay was born in October 1996 in Zhejiang Province in China. On 23 February 1998, when she was 17 months old, she joined her adoptive family in Hangzhou, one of China's most beautiful cities, famed for the West Lake. Josephine returned to China with her parents in October 2005 and they visited the children's institute where she had lived for 15 months and the village where she was originally found. She met the

people who had discovered her who expressed great joy that she was strong and healthy. It was a very happy occasion with many of the villagers coming to see her. Josephine attends South Hampstead High School in London and her favourite subjects are art, design and technology and maths. She is happiest when painting in her room while listening to Harry Potter. She loves animals and likes playing with her longhaired dachshund Ziggy.

Josh was born in Dublin in 2001. He is of Irish and African parentage. Before joining his white Irish adoptive family he lived with a foster family from birth to seven months. Josh has one younger brother, Mark, who is also adopted and of Irish and African parentage. Josh has some limited contact with his birth family. He enjoys cooking, cycling and has an avid interest in cars and all things mechanical. He is happiest when he is planning holidays and travelling abroad. Josh hopes to be a pilot when he grows up and to take all his family on great holidays! Josh lives in County Clare, in the west of Ireland.

Joshua was born in Bangkok, the capital of Thailand, in January 1996. Having been born premature and of low birth weight, he spent the first nine months of his life in a children's hospital before being transferred to Pakkret Babies Home, just outside Bangkok. The home houses 500 children from birth to the age of five. His mum and dad adopted him in November 1997 when he was 22 months old. Joshua has been back to Thailand four times, the most important occasion being in the summer of 2006 when he met his birth father and other relatives. With his mum and dad he attended the Nativeland Visit which is organised by the Thai government every three years.

Joshua enjoys reading, playing hockey and computer, and has recently learned to make movies. He is happiest when he is at home with his parents and hopes to become a lawyer. Joshua lives in London.

Julia was born at the end of 1992 in England. She was fostered, then adopted. The only biological family member she has contact with is her eldest sister who is not adopted and this is by letter. Julia loves her adoptive parents whom she considers to be her "real" parents. She loves playing sport and being with her friends. When she is older she would like to be a policewoman, a mother and a sailing instructor for disabled children. After achieving all these things, Julia would like to be a foster carer so that she can give children another chance in life, just as she was.

Karen Ulyana Roche was born in June 1999 in the Russian city of Orsk. Her first eight months were spent in a baby home until she was adopted by her Irish parents. Karen now lives happily in the southeast of Ireland. Karen is fully aware of her dual heritage and enjoys learning about the country of her birth. Her many interests include Irish dancing, piano lessons, drama, swimming and attending classes on Russian culture. Always eager to learn, Karen has a great capacity for retaining information and loves school. Her ambition, from an early age, is to become a doctor..

Katie was born in 1998 in Yorkshire and is of white British parentage. She went into care at six months old and lived with three sets of foster carers before finally moving to her adoptive family when she was two. During her time in foster care she had regular contact with her birth mother. Since moving to her adoptive family she has sent letters to her via the social services postbox system. Katie loves animals, especially horses and her border terrier dog Cleo. She is happiest being in charge and is definitely a leader not a follower! She has a very caring nature and would like to become a vet or a nurse when she grows up. She loves spending time with her immediate adoptive family, grandparents and "extended family" of adopted friends. Katie lives in England.

Kevin Toni Mitchell was born in Leeds, England in 1985 to a Jamaican father and white British mother. In 1987, at the age of two-and-a-half, he was adopted into a white family who had one other adopted dual heritage child. Kevin has strong feelings on the subject of transracial adoption and would like to be able to share them and have people understand what it is like to be "placed" in someone else's family. He was always acutely aware of the fact that he didn't belong where he was and this wasn't helped by being so obviously unrelated to the rest of the family (by being black). Kevin was provided with everything a child could wish for really and he feels ashamed and ungrateful to say that it wasn't enough, that none of his parents' efforts would ever be enough. He now lives in the Midlands on his own and sees them maybe three or four times a year.

Kevin enjoys writing poetry and has also received support through Adoption Support. He currently works in a bank as a senior adviser. Kevin is also studying part time for a law degree through the Open University. In what little time Kevin does have between working and studying he enjoys playing rugby for a local side where he plays on the wing. Though Kevin quite enjoys working hard, studying, getting certificates and passing exams, no amount of qualifications will make him feel better about having been given away by the most important person in the world to him.

KB was born in Hunan province in China in 1998. She was adopted when she was 12 months old and then came home to live in England. She has a mum and dad, a big brother and two big sisters. One of her big sisters was also adopted from China. KB is hoping to go back to China next year. She loves shopping and dressing up.

Kerri was born in England in 1996. She is proud to say that she has been adopted and is happily living with her mum, dad and sister. She loves riding and playing golf and being with her pony. She is also proud to say that she usually has lots to say about lots of things. She works hard and is very determined to be successful in her future life. She keeps in contact with her beloved gran and granddad and her big 'bro' Charlie – he is the best!

Kyle was born in 1995 in the north of England. Kyle and all of his birth siblings have all come into care. Kyle came into care with three siblings when he was four years old. He was placed with very good foster carers before being adopted. Kyle and his sisters have been adopted together. His older sister and a younger brother have each been adopted by separate families in different parts of the country. He sees this sister twice a year but sadly has no contact with his younger brother. This lack of contact with his brother upsets Kyle greatly. He lives with his mum and dad, and his sister, two cats and Meg, the dog, in a village in northern England. Kyle tries his best at school. He is a member of a gymnastics club, Scouts and a football club which leaves him little time for his homework! He is happiest playing football in the field behind his home with his mate from next door, horse riding or clay pigeon shooting. If he cannot play football for Aston Villa, Kyle would like to be a policeman.

Leon "City" Davis was born 1987 of Jamaican and English heritage. He wrote this verse for his younger brothers to say that, although things with their "mum" didn't work out, he still loves them whatever has or will happen and even with them not being together right now, he is there for them.

Lê Văn Thanh was born in Ho Chi Minh City, Vietnam in 1997 and adopted by his British parents in December 1998, when he was 14 months old. He visited Vietnam in 2007 and is really looking forward to another trip in 2009. He is happiest going on long bike rides with his dad and granddad. He hopes to drive a van when he grows up. Văn Thanh lives in England.

Lex Wolf was born in Bucharest, Romania on 22 September 1987. He came to England on 16 July 1996, shortly before his ninth birthday. Lex was adopted by a single mother who has since married and had a birth child, who is now five years old. Lex has been back to Romania once and visited one of his three children's homes. He works as a hall porter in a hotel and enjoys dance, especially hip-hop and breakdancing.

Luis was born in Guatemala. He came to his new family in London at seven months old in 1995. He lives with his dad, mum and older brother (also adopted), is a fanatical War Hammer painter and player, a whizz at dancing, loves music, maths, art and chess. He has wanted to be an architect since he was three. For the moment, he is certain that he does not want contact with his birth family but he feels he might when he grows up. The family has visited Central America on holiday where Luis thoroughly enjoyed scaling Mayan temples.

Luke Howard was born in 1997 in London and is of dual heritage. He joined his adoptive family at the age of one day, straight from hospital following his birth. He had no health issues until the age of six when he developed Chronic Recurring Multifocal Osteomyalitis. This is an extremely rare bone condition that has caused him to have spells of immobility which has made him very angry at times. From being a very able rugby player and sporty type he has developed other more academic skills to compensate. He now plays the guitar and is very able at reading and writing for his age. Luke lives in England.

Mack was born in 1995 in London and is of Irish and Scottish parentage. He was four years old when he joined his adoptive family and has some limited contact with his birth father. Mack likes football and being on the computer with his friends. He lives in England.

Marcus Wootton-Kahn was born in 1987 in north London. He came into care when he was eight years old, went to an emergency carer for one week, and then came to Helen who finally adopted him when he was 16. He wanted this to happen. Marcus lives at home in London with his mum and attends college. He loves drama, relaxing and travelling and dreams of becoming a famous actor.

Marina Harris was born in Bolivia in 1995. The fifth surviving child in her birth family, she joined her adoptive mum when she was two months old, coming to live in London at ten months. Marina does not have contact with her birth family, but visited Bolivia when she was five. Her favourite activities are dancing, dressmaking and cooking. She hopes to eventually go to art school to study design. Marina is happiest when she is hanging out with her friends.

Marisa Midian Lucero was born in Antigua, Guatemala, in September 1999. She joined her adoptive family when she was nine months old and lives near Oxford with her mum, dad and four-year-old sister Natalia, also from Guatemala. Marisa has contact with her birth mother by letter and has met her as well as her sister, brother and grandparents since being adopted. Marisa likes to talk about Guatemala and is starting to take an interest in its history. She enjoys swimming, roller-skating and ballet and loves animals.

Michael was born in Wales in the mid-1990s and joined his adoptive family at 14 months. His passions are art, music and drama. Michael lives with his adoptive parents and sister who was adopted when he was five years old.

Millie was born in England in 1997 of English parents. She was fostered at three-and-a-half years and joined her adoptive family when she was five. Her sister, Georgie, was adopted by the same family; her younger brother was adopted by a different family and they are in touch. Millie now lives outside of the UK. Millie loves to dance – she likes to float and twirl around the kitchen to her favourite music. She also loves to play her Nintendo DS. She is at her happiest when she is playing with her cousins or visiting her brother.

Milo Howard is the youngest of 16 children (six are adopted). He was born in Nottingham and is of dual parentage. Milo has learning and behavioural issues. Anyone who meets Milo will enjoy his company as there is never a dull moment. He is a very sociable and outgoing child who loves school and is determined to make the best of every opportunity. He has friends at school and the highlight of his week is being invited to a friend's home for tea. Milo loves playing with his puppies. He has no contact with

his birth family and lives in England.

Muireann was born in 1997 in County Monaghan, Ireland. She was fostered with a view to adoption at five months and was subsequently adopted. Muireann lives with her mum and dad and her older sister in rural Ireland where the family keeps many pets. She and her sister are very close. She does not yet have any contact with her birth family. Muireann is very good at school and at Irish dancing, to which she accompanies her older sister, a champion dancer. Muireann loves animals and in particular enjoys riding a pony borrowed from a neighbour. She is happiest when playing with school friends and cousins of similar age. Muireann talks about becoming a vet when she is older.

Naila was born in 2000. She is dual heritage, Pakistani and White British. She went into care at birth from the hospital. She joined her adoptive parents aged eight months. She has letterbox contact with her birth mother and visits her foster family. Her adoptive family consists of an Asian mother and a white mother, a 21-year-old Asian sister who was adopted in the UK at the age of eight and is now at university, and a middle Asian sister, aged 11, who is hearing impaired and was adopted in the UK at 16 months. Naila enjoys designing and making things and is happiest when she is playing makebelieve with her friends and sister. She lives in the UK.

Nathan Glazier was born in 1994 in England and is of white English parentage. He and his sister were adopted by their foster carers in 2000. As well as a sister, Nathan has younger twin siblings in his adoptive family. He lives in London. Nathan loves acting and likes spending time with his mates. They mainly go into town and look around the shops. Nathan likes poetry and enjoys writing it.

Oisin Ruslan was born in 2003 in Orenburg, Russia. He was in an orphanage until the age of six months when he joined his adoptive family in Ireland. His adoptive family consists of his mam and dad and an older brother, Eoin, who was adopted

from Romania. He has not visited Russia again and he does not have any contact with his birth family. Oisin enjoys television, hurling, football and the swings. He is happiest when he is eating sweets. He hopes to get all the Thomas the Train Collection and to go to Russia some day. Oisin lives in Oldcastletown, County Cork, Ireland.

Ossie Whitehead was born in Guatemala in 1997 and joined his adoptive family on Christmas day 1999 (three weeks before his third birthday). He lives in west London with his mum Elly, dad Stevan and sister Veronica. He has contact with his birth mother and extended family as well as with his foster family. Ossie is a natural sportsman enjoying football, rugby and karate among others. The whole family went back to Guatemala in summer

2006 and met the foster family and Ossie's birth family. They plan to return in 2009.

Phan Thi Mỹ Liên was born in Ho Chi Minh City, Vietnam in June 2000 and joined her British adoptive family at eight weeks. She has an older brother who was also born in Vietnam. Mỹ Liên really enjoys school and her favourite subject is English. In the summer of 2007 she visited Vietnam and had a great time.

Rebecca Glazier was born in 1996 in England and is of white English parentage. She and her brother Nathan were adopted by their foster carers in 2000. As well as a brother, Rebecca has younger twin siblings in her adoptive family. Rebecca's hobbies are dancing, acting, swimming, gymnastics and Guides. She loves being with friends and family and adores animals. She lives in London.

Ronan was born in 2003 in Kirovohrad, Ukraine. He joined his adoptive family when he was 15 months old and, at the age of three-and-a-half, travelled with his mother to meet and bring home his baby sister Brannagh from Vietnam. Ronan really likes travelling and particularly aeroplanes, although buses and trains are great too. He recently started school and enjoys writing. Ronan does not have contact with his birth family which he is quite sad about. He wishes he did. He likes animals very much and has three dogs and a cat.

Rosie was born in London in 2001. She is a white English child whose father is Scottish. Rosie was subject to a care order at birth and lived the first four months of her life in hospital as she was very ill. She had little stimulation and was never taken outside until the day when her adoptive parents collected her and brought her home to live with them. Rosie joined her bother Rowan who is four years older and was also adopted as a baby at

ten months. Rosie does not have any contact with her birth family as they seem to have disappeared. Rosie is very upset about this situation and especially longs to see her mother. She finds it particularly hard as Rowan has contact with his mother and sisters. Rowan helped Rosie in writing the poem and he also has plans to hire a private detective to search for Rosie's birth mother as soon as he can. Rosie has recently been assessed and it is clear that she has serious attachment issues which her family is trying to help her with. Despite all of this, Rosie is an extrovert, vibrant and passionate child with limitless energy and enthusiasm. She enjoys all sport, especially gymnastics, and loves to climb and dance. She also loves to read and write her own stories. She is very popular with older children whom she entertains with her cheeky behaviour and chav impersonations! Rosie would most like to have her own kitten to care for and for the future hopes to have contact with her birth family, particularly her mother.

Ruby was born in 2000 in the People's Republic of China and joined her adoptive family when she was two. In the family she has two older sisters as well as her mum and dad. They live in the Midlands. Ruby visited China again in 2008. Now aged seven, she loves drawing and painting and wants to be an artist one day.

Ruth Ling Dooley was born in late 2000 (barely a millennium baby) in China. She joined her adoptive family in 2002, at one year old, a few weeks after her first birthday. She has no knowledge of or contact with her birth family but she has stayed in touch with her foster carers. Ruth enjoys swimming, acting, music and reading, but is happiest when she is making things or playing chess with her parents. She loves painting and being creative. Her  dreams for the future are to become a vet and a beekeeper. She lives in Ireland.

Samantha was born in the southwest of England in 1995 and went into care when she was six years old. She spent 18 months with foster carers before joining her adoptive family at the age of seven. Her family consists of mum and dad and two older brothers. She has no contact with her birth family. She is now a very happy 12-year-old who loves life and makes the most of her opportunities. She works hard at school, plays the piano, loves to cook, enjoys walking the dog and is a complete star with one of her brothers who is disabled. She rarely complains, always looks on the bright side and is very much loved and has made her family complete.

Sasha was born in Ethiopia in 2003 and adopted soon after by her mummy and daddy from Ireland. She is now five-and-a-half years old and has just finished her first year of primary school. She lives with her family in the country.

Smurfy was fostered from the age of nine then moved in with her adoptive family (nice people really!) when she was 12. She was then adopted officially when she was 13. Yes, she is still alive (and surviving!). Smurfy sees her brothers once a year individually and then they have one big altogether rave in the summer (very tiring!). Her hobbies and interests are trampolining, gymnastics and playing the piano. Smurfy likes chocolate and anything sweet! She dislikes spiders IMMENSELY!!! Smurfy enjoys performing on stage and is part of a local amateur dramatics group. She is currently studying for ten GCSEs.

Sobia was born in 1996. She is dual heritage, Pakistani and white British. She is hearing impaired and has an auditory processing disorder. She went into care at three weeks and joined her adoptive parents aged 16 months. She has letterbox contact with her birth mother, birth father and maternal grandmother, and visits her foster family. Her adoptive family consists of an Asian mother and a white mother, an older Asian sister aged 21 who was adopted in the UK aged eight and is now at university and a younger Asian sister who was adopted in the UK at eight months. Sobia enjoys swimming and is a member of her local swimming club. She is happiest when she is horse riding and hopes to work with animals when she is older. She lives in the UK.

Sola was born in 1995 in England. She is white British and was adopted at the age of six years, after being in care with her two siblings. All three were adopted into separate families. Sola has a very negative view and experience of maintaining contact with one sister whose new family do not want the visits to take place. She lives in the south of England.

Solome was born in Ethiopia in July 1999. She lived in Kidane Meheret until she was four-and-a-half months old before joining her adoptive family in Ireland. She has an older and younger brother, both adopted from Ethiopia. Solome has visited her country of birth three times since her adoption. She loves Ethiopian *injera*, particularly with *lamb tibs* and loves to dress in Ethiopian dress. She enjoys art, dancing and music, and is happiest when she is with family and friends.

Sophie was born in 2000 in England and joined her adoptive family when she was five years old. She enjoys going to Brownies, swimming, riding her scooter and going to school.

Sophie was born in 1995. She has lived with her adoptive family, together with her sister Kerri, since August 2006. She sees her brother Charlie regularly and has also kept in touch with her former foster carer whom both she and her sister dearly love. She stayed with her for a week in the summer of 2007. Sophie loves animals, particularly rats and horses. She has two pet rats called MnM and Squeakles and looks after several horses with her friend. Sophie has made lots of new friends at her new home and loves "chillin' out" with them.

Terezia Dziubak was born Terezia-Luliana Lakatos in 1987. Her mother, a Romany, and her father, a Hungarian, were very young and without income. There was nowhere within the extended family for Terezia and she was put into an orphanage at birth where she lived until she was three-and-a-half. She was then adopted and became Terezia-Luliana O'Curry, and embarked on a sharp learning curve of language and socialisation into British life. When she was six her adoptive parents brought over two of her sisters from another orphanage in Romania. Social workers involved at the time were strongly opposed to the further adoption. From this point in time family life became very difficult and a downward spiral commenced. Terezia's preoccupation with gaining a bond with her adoptive mother was deeply entrenched, as her adoptive mother was so "wrapped up" with Terezia's two sisters' needs. The emotional hole left in Terezia by her first mother's abandonment and her second mother's "betrayal" undermined her education and all her early relationships.

Terezia left home at 16 in acrimonious circumstances, but gained help from a local housing charity. They helped her to enroll at college and think of her future as well as find housing. She began to make friends and feel a little more sense of her own identity. Terezia moved on from trying to have a relationship with her adoptive mother and found comfort, warmth and true love with an older man, Rodney Dzuibak R.I.P. He died of a brain haemorrhage in April 2008, just before their son's first birthday. Rodney taught Terezia what true love is and how to trust but she is still unable to forgive others.

Throughout Terezia's life when things got tough, she turned to her music by playing the violin and piano, to escape the pain and anger that she felt. As she got older she composed her own music and went on to create videos to help her overcome the sudden traumatic death of Rodney. Terezia is able to remain positive and strong for the sake of her son and Rodney's family who Terezia regards as her family too. She has now moved into a two-bedroom flat with her son and, with help, is very positive about the future ahead.

Veronica Whitehead was born in 1998 in Guatemala and joined her adoptive family in the summer of 1999. She lives in west London with her mum Elly, dad Stevan and brother Ossie. She has contact with her foster family whom she shared with her brother for a year. Veronica plays the flute and enjoys judo and capoiera. The whole family went back to Guatemala in summer 2006 and met the foster family and Ossie's birth family. They plan to return in 2009.

Victoria is 14 and white British. She joined her adoptive family around four years ago, along with her sister, and has some contact with her siblings. Victoria likes to spend time with friends, enjoys networking on the computer, horse riding, dancing and singing. She lives in England.

Zoe (Lin Xiuji) Macrae, born November 2000, was adopted from China in 2001. Zoe now lives in southern England with her older sister, also adopted from China, and her Scottish parents. Zoe loves reading, playing the viola, swimming and tennis. She ADORES playparks in China!

Useful websites

Here are some key sites for people who are adopted, adoptive parents or those interested in adopting, or birth relatives of an adopted person. They will lead you to other sources of information including details of adoption agencies, adoption support agencies and support groups, and relevant resources and publications.

Adoption, Search and Reunion: www.adoptionsearchreunion.org.uk

This website is for anyone thinking about searching for or making contact with birth and adopted relatives. It includes databases on the location of adoption records and adoption support agencies, and information on the legal rights of all parties.

Adoption UK: www.adoptionuk.org.uk

Adoption UK is a self-help charity run by and for adoptive parents and foster carers. It provides support, information and advice for people considering adoption, going through the process or established as an adoptive family.

Adults Affected by Adoption-NORCAP: www.norcap.org.uk

AAA-NORCAP supports adopted adults wishing to find out about their birth family, birth relatives seeking contact with their adult child who has been adopted, and adoptive parents whose children are searching for birth relatives.

British Association for Adoption and Fostering: www.baaf.org.uk

The BAAF site contains information for people considering adopting or who are adoptive parents; details of the legal and policy framework in England, Wales, Scotland and Northern Ireland; and publications for children and adoptive parents.

Natural Parents Network: www.n-p-n.co.uk

NPN is a UK-based self-help organisation, which offers non-judgemental, confidential and independent support to parents and relatives who have lost children to adoption.

New Family Social: www.newfamilysocial.co.uk

This is a group run for and by lesbian and gay adoptive parents.

The Adoption Authority of Ireland: www.adoptionboard.ie

This site contains information about domestic and intercountry adoption in Ireland, including intercountry adoption support groups for adoptive parents.

Overseas Adoption Information and Support Service: www.adoptionoverseas.org

OASIS is a UK-based support group for people who wish to adopt, or have already adopted from another country.

TALK Adoption: www.afteradoption.org.uk

This is a national helpline for young people under 26 who want to talk about adoption. It is for young people who are: adopted; waiting to be adopted; young birth parents whose child/ren have been adopted; brothers or sisters of an adopted child/ren; or friends with young people involved in adoption. Call free on 0808 808 1234.

Transnational and Transracial Adoption Group: www.ttag.org.uk

TTAG is a network run by and for transnationally and transracially adopted adults.